Dear Wellbeing...

100 Days on My Path
to More Joy

★ Also By Susan Balogh ★

BOOKS
100 Days of Actions & Intentions to Create the Life You Wish For
https://www.amazon.com/dp/B099PZC9T1

There's MAGIC in this MANIFESTING JOURNAL: It's Your Imagination
http://amzn.com/B0967TRMSF

FREE MINI-WORKSHOP
3 Steps to Wellbeing & Achieving Your Dreams
https://courses.wishmorewellness.com/courses/Mini-Workshop-3-Steps

ONLINE COURSE
Create the Life You Wish For: A 100-Day Course
https://courses.wishmorewellness.com

ONLINE SERVICES
1:1 Coaching for Mindset/Happiness/Manifesting
Positive EFT Coaching (Meridian Tapping)
Energy Healing, Guided Meditation
Reiki I & II and Master/Teacher Certification
All or part available by video conference

Set Yourself Free & Be Happy!

★★★

All of the above are available at
wishmorewellness.com/services/
Find us on Instagram @Wishmore_Wellness
https://www.instagram.com/wishmore_wellness/
Please join the Wishmore Wellness Facebook Group
https://www.facebook.com/groups/2061444523962316

Dear Wellbeing...

100 Days on My Path to More Joy

A Self-Discovery Workbook

Susan Balogh

Cover design: Angie Alaya
Interior design: Rachael Cox
Illustrations by Streamline Design

ISBN eBook: 978-1-7361677-0-0
ISBN Paperback: 978-1-7361677-1-7

Published by Wishmore Wellness
Buffalo, NY
WishmoreWellness.com
First printing, November 2020
Printed in the United States of America

★

This

book is

dedicated to

those of you who

are ready to let yourself

shine through the many layers

of life's little (or big) struggles. It's

time for you to be in charge of your own

wellbeing and practice feeling the way

you deserve to feel. And that is in

your natural state of blissful

wellbeing. And if you

found yourself

here, you're

ready!

★

Take 100 Days to Guide Yourself There.
I know you can do it. And you're worth it!

Set Yourself Free & Be Happy!

Wish*More Wellness' mission is to help as many people as possible reconnect with their true nature and powerful ability to heal, to love, and to create the life they wish for.

The name WISH*More Wellness is all about how our Words Inspire Spiritual Harmony & More Wellness...for ourselves and others.

When we take charge of our thoughts in a more positive and purposeful way, we can talk ourselves into anything. Living a life with more wellbeing, joy, and abundance is a choice.

Harmony of your mind, body, and spirit is the direct route to healing and happiness.

Let each kind word, thought, and action begin with you and create a better life for you and those around you, one moment at a time. Your positive energy will spread beyond boundaries.

Table of Contents

Hello & Welcome to Your 100 Day Workbook!
How to Get the Most Out of This Workbook
My Promise to Myself

One Last Pep Talk
Recommended Reading
About the Author

Hello & Welcome to Your 100-Day Workbook

You have the ability to feel your way into any reality you wish to exist in. You can think how you want to think and feel how you want to feel and even get your body to respond in the way that you want it to.

You can literally talk yourself into anything. It just takes practice. And that's what this workbook is meant to help you do.

Imagine being in the qualities and energy of your highest level of wellbeing and becoming the joyful person you were born to be. That is, a person who feels deeply satisfied with who they are and where their life is going. It's in this good-feeling place where you align with all your desires and bring them to life.

When you've brought your mind and body into harmony with the natural free spirit within you, you allow the wellbeing to flow, and when it flows, all good things come your way with effortless ease. The possibilities are limitless.

Perhaps more consistency in your invincible mindset is all you ever needed to help you get from where you are to where you want to be. Sometimes it's just a matter of practicing a mindset long enough to let it become a part of who you are. And that's why this book is 100 days long. The goal is to create a habit that lasts a lifetime.

Rather than thinking about making a radical change to improve your life, or wishing for it, as many of us do (including myself!), you're going to actually do the work. Only it doesn't feel like work. Self-discovery is so much fun!

As you navigate your way through this fully interactive workbook, you will practice feeling your way into the mindset that helps you achieve a higher level of wellbeing, as well as your desires for all areas of your life: home, family, career, and all your goals and dreams.

It will often feel as though you're playing a role: the role of who you *want* to be. But that feeling is available to you *right now*. And it's in this *feeling* place where you will find yourself achieving your desires. As you align your energy with them, they are yours to have.

There's another wonderful thing that happens when you're focusing your attention on what you truly want in life. Any unwanted thoughts, beliefs, or potential problems easily fall away. You begin to notice that the more lighthearted you feel, the more you attract positive people, conversations, and moments throughout your day.

Your mind and body are responding to your thoughts and direction, and before long, you've learned to master your emotions. This can be the way things are for you. Your thoughts and intentions are that powerful!

While the primary focus in the beginning of the book will be on your general wellbeing, the topic changes every ten days to cover a desired outcome you have for each area of your life.

It is my wish that you make it your one-pointed focus to be in the harmony and wellbeing that's natural to you until it becomes the only way you know how to be. Life becomes more effortless and before you know it, everything you want begins to unfold in the most glorious way. It's how life is meant to be, and you truly deserve to feel that good.

Truth be told, I wrote this book for myself as much as I wrote it for you. We all need a little guidance and support once in a while. But as someone who has gone through it all - daily pain and struggle and living a life that wasn't aligned with my true desires for what seemed like a *zillion* years - I eventually found myself in a wonderful-feeling place, and knew I wanted to help others get there much faster than I did.

It was an easy decision to leave my office job and become a holistic healing and happiness coach. I love following my heart and I will encourage *you* to do the same. And when I coach or write *anything*, I *love* to do what I can to evoke every possible emotion in you to attain the mindset that will help you achieve any goal you may have.

When following the steps offered in this workbook, I believe you will see and feel results. How much and for how long is up to you. I believe you deserve to be deeply satisfied and feel like celebrating your life *every single day.*

By nature...you are in a state of blissful wellbeing, and it's time for you to let it in.

So, let's begin, shall we? 100 days may seem like a long time to dedicate your time, but you're so worth it! And you can take it at your own pace. Just remember to let it be fun!

How to Get the Most Out of This Workbook

Consider doing this at the same place and time every day. It can be a great way to start or end the day, whichever is most convenient.

For the Kindle version, be sure to have a journal or notebook to write your answers in, of course. The paperback has plenty of space to write your answers.

Complete the 100 days in as few days as possible; ideally completing a "Day" chapter every day, or every second or third day. This is to keep your positive momentum going.

The many questions you will be asked as you work through this book are to get you thinking about all your potential and possibilities...

Your subconscious naturally wants to answer the questions, and your mind and body respond to the suggestions.

You may feel the proposed buildup of anticipation for what's to come, and with some practice you can feel your energy or mindset shifting to another level.

It's a great way to transform emotions that are more set-in from old thought patterns. It may feel as though you're repeating the same answers at times, and that's fine. The idea is to practice guiding your thoughts.

Allow yourself to be your most creative and convincing self as you write the answers that first come to mind. You may find it easier to answer as though you're writing to your best friend.

Always write freely on any subject if the one you're on does not apply to you or isn't feeling right. Let it be easy and fun for you. And if privacy is a concern, put your workbook in a safe place. ☺

Do your best to fill in every line throughout your workbook with as many answers as you can come up with. The more you write, the more inspired you can feel, and the more aligned you become with the energy of wellbeing or the desire you're writing about.

For any of your desires: rather than feeling that you're trying to achieve something that's unattainable, feel that they're already yours to have.

You become what you believe you can be. Move forward with complete faith and purpose, and you will achieve any desire you wish. You are now becoming energetically aligned with all of it. I know you can do it. Do you? If not now, you will.

My Promise to Myself

(Feel free to change the wording to match your desires)

I decided that *I am now* allowing myself the freedom and right to be in the natural state I was born to be in.

Wellbeing is natural to me and my body has the ability to clear anything that needs to be healed. I am simply attuning to the frequency of my natural state of wellbeing. I can do this by practicing the feeling of wellbeing until it feels like a part of me and it's who I am. I see nothing else. I hear nothing else. And I think of nothing that will oppose this.

My body responds to my consistent thoughts of wellbeing, and when I notice how much better I'm feeling, my belief gets stronger. I feel empowered in my ability to feel any way I wish to feel.

I begin to feel invincible. As I practice my alignment with wellbeing, there's no other way for me to be. Nothing but the thought of wellbeing will ever come to mind. I'm feeling well and feel certain that I always will.

With my unwavering faith, I think it, feel it, and believe in it, and make it mine. It must become my reality.

This is how powerful my thoughts and intentions are. I can create anything I wish to be or have or do. I am meant to feel good all day, every day. And that is what I intend to do.

I am now achieving alignment with my highest level of wellbeing.

The more positive my thoughts and emotions, the better I feel and the higher my vibration. The higher my vibration, the closer I am to achieving *all* my desires.

I intend to practice guiding myself to a good-feeling place until I'm struggle-free and living the joyful life I'm meant to be living.

I Am Setting Powerful Intentions for My Wellbeing and Desired Outcomes

Here's what I promise to do in order to align with my highest level of wellbeing. I will do my best to:

* ★ Practice a state of total wellbeing
* ★ Take my attention away from anything that's not going well as much as possible
* ★ Acknowledge and release any worries, fears, or limiting beliefs
* ★ Take time to connect with my body and my breath
* ★ Find the feeling of ease as often as I can
* ★ Be my best supporter
* ★ Honor and nurture my body
* ★ Continually guide my thoughts to a good-feeling place
* ★ Take responsibility for my wellbeing
* ★ Follow my path to more joy
* ★ Remember to have fun along the way!

I am now creating a life where I feel good from morning to night in *every* way. If not now, I'm going to envision it and feel my way into it until it's mine and it's what I'm living. The strength of my desire for it and my faith and trust and belief in it are arranging it all for me. No matter how good I feel now, I'm *always* able to feel even better.

What I *believe* is possible is the extent of what I can make happen. So there's no end to what I can do if I believe in it. I have access to *all* possibility.

During the next 100 days, I am committed to allowing myself to begin a potentially life-changing transformation. I am open to discovering more about myself and perhaps some new desires along the way.

Right now I believe I am perfect right where I am. I am exactly where I'm meant to be at this time in my life, and I'm always moving toward a better place. I am in a constant state of change and becoming better every day in every way.

From this day forward, I intend to spend every precious moment of my life thinking and saying and doing what's in alignment with my true desires. My thoughts, intentions, energy, and actions are creating my life, and I intend to use them to the best of my ability to live a life I love more every day.

Add any intentions, affirmations, or notes that you wish...

_____

_____

_____

_____

_____

_____

_____

_____

_____

_____

_____

_____

_____

_____

_____

_____

_____

_____

_____

_____

_____

If desired, sign here as a declaration of your commitment to making the positive changes that you, yourself, are choosing: _____

★ I Am Committed to Living a Life I Love More Every Day!

So how do I want my life to go? Where am I now, and where do I want to be? Do I wish to make any changes? I'm going to write a wish list in a moment, but here are some things to consider first.

> If I could have anything I want right now in this moment, what would I choose?
> In what ways do I wish to feel better than I do right now?
> Do I want more energy to do the things I love to do?
> Do I want to feel happier throughout my day?
> Do I want to feel more ease in my body?
> Do I want a clearer mind or to feel more peaceful?
> Do I want to make any changes in my body or health?
> Do I want to improve my relationships, and if so, in what way?
> Do I want to make changes in my work or social life?
> How would I feel after the changes?

How does it feel when I allow myself to feel the wellbeing flowing to me? Take a moment and close your eyes and think of the things that you want for your overall wellbeing. Take yourself there and feel how it would feel to be living it. Stop reading and do this now.

Now you're ready to write out your wish list.

A Wish List for Improving My Overall Wellbeing

Write the desired end result you want for the following areas:

My Health is: _____

My Mind is: _____

My Body looks and feels: _____

I am Feeling: _____

My Home and Family are: _____

My Relationship is: _____

My Work Life is: _____

My Personal Life is: _____

My Dreams and Plans are: _____

My Ideal Future is: _____

After you're done, circle the desires that feel really good when you think about them. See the end result in your mind and how you would look and feel when you've achieved them. Think of this image often or just before going to sleep, as desired.

Now, read these questions and take a moment to contemplate each one before writing how you believe it will feel:

When I've achieved my desire for more blissful wellbeing, how does it feel?

_____

What does my life look like when I've achieved everything on my wish list?

_____

How does it feel to be living it? Can I see it and imagine how it would feel to be there?

_____

What qualities or characteristics do I have?

_____

How does it feel to have more energy?

_____

How does it feel to give myself permission to feel good all the time?

_____

How does it feel when I allow myself to feel blissful?

_____

Close your eyes and ask that last question again. Give your body and energy time to respond. Relax and breathe in extra slow at first and put your attention on your face. Repeat the question a few more times, and say it very slowly with the emphasis on the word allow. Feel as though you're breathing in this blissful energy. It's almost as though a blanket of golden energy has been placed upon your chest and over your face, and you're just breathing that heavenly feeling in. Or think of something that has brought you so much joy in your life and breathe it in. What would that feel like?

If not now, with a little practice I will begin to feel the effects of guiding my thoughts and be able to feel any way I wish to feel. Even when my life's pretty great, there's always a way to make it even better. And from now on I focus on solutions. As I practice guiding my thoughts to a better-feeling state in the weeks or months ahead, I'm looking forward to living a life I love more every day. I am open and receptive to further self-discovery and all the gifts that life has in store for me. This is my powerful intention.

I am now achieving a state of blissful wellbeing. How does it feel when I *allow* myself to feel blissful today and every day? *Your homework is to ask yourself this question every morning. If it feels good, ask it as often as you'd like.*

Intentions for My Day (Or tomorrow if it's late)

If I could have my day be how I wanted it to be, what would it be like? What are the words that describe it? I am feeling _____. I am being _____. I am having _____. I am doing _____. How will I look and feel at the end of the day?

_____

_____

_____

Imagine it now.

Always feel free to write a full page of answers in a notebook or journal for this particular exercise.

For the next nine days, the topic will mainly be on what you wrote on Day 1 as your desired end result for...

My Health is: _____. Please fill it in once again. You are allowing your natural state of total wellbeing to be a part of who you are. The more it feels that way, the more it becomes so. Imagine you're having a conversation with yourself or with a symbol that represents your utmost health. Tell it what you want, why you want it, what it will do for you when you have it, and how it will change your life. Fill the page with as many details as possible. Speak from the heart, and write the first words that come to mind and keep going.

Dear Wellbeing,

_____
_____
_____
_____
_____
_____
_____
_____
_____
_____
_____
_____
_____
_____
_____
_____
_____
_____
_____
_____
_____
_____

It's important to keep my desired end result in mind. Once I've achieved my desire for even better health, what am I doing differently? How do I think I would be acting and feeling?

I am spending more time thinking about...

_____

Emotionally, I am feeling...

_____

Physically, I am feeling...

_____

I am feeling more confident about...

_____

I am feeling more connected to myself because...

_____

I am being...

_____

I am having more fun doing...

_____

I am doing more of what I wish to do. I am...

_____

My life feels better because I am...

_____

I love my body's ability to heal and bring itself into balance. I love knowing that it's functioning perfectly. I love that I'm giving myself permission to feel as good as I can feel. And I love giving my body the joy and ease it deserves. There's no limit to the amount of wellbeing I can achieve. I am focusing on my inevitable success in achieving a higher level of wellbeing. I am holding a mental image of myself in the highest level of joy and wellbeing. I am practicing it until it's all I know. All that I know to be true for me. _If desired, close your eyes and see it and feel it. See yourself with your arms open wide and receptive to this path that's all lit up for you._

All my desires want me as much as I want them. The moment I have a desire, it begins taking form and all I need to do is stay out of the way by finding as much ease and joy as I can. I am now aligning with the energy of total wellbeing. _Your turn_: I am _____.

What is your favorite part about your current state of wellbeing and why?

_____

_____

_____

_____

_____

Intentions for My Day (Or tomorrow)

What words describe my day? I am feeling _____. I am being _____. I am having _____. I am doing _____. How will I look and feel at the end of the day? Imagine it now.

Total wellbeing is available to me right now. As I move forward with faith and purpose and believe and expect it to come, I am able to achieve it with ease. I am becoming what I believe I can be.

What does total wellbeing mean to me?

_____

How do I get there? To begin with, I am creating an atmosphere for success. I am practicing what I can do to allow it to flow into my life. Doing something different than how I've been doing it will create different results.

Does it feel like anything needs to happen, mentally, emotionally, or physically in order for me to align with this now? Let's begin by checking in and making peace with where I am. What is going really well in relation to my health?

_____

_____

I feel healthiest when I am...

_____

My greatest achievements or strengths in relation to my health have been...

_____

_____

The habits or activities I enjoy that support my health and I plan to continue are...

_____

_____

I wish to improve on...

_____

The habits or activities that are not feeling right and I prefer to stop doing once I'm feeling ready are...

_____

_____

Does my physical environment support my desire for better health? Is there anything I would like to replace with something that brings me more joy or soothes me in some way?

_____

_____

If I had a magic wand, what changes would I make in relation to my general health?

_____

_____

_____

How would this change my life?

_____

_____

_____

I believe an even healthier body is achievable for me because...

_____

_____

What state of mind do I think I need to be in to achieve it? What are some new thoughts I could practice to align with the energy of my best health?

_____

_____

_____

If I'm experiencing any health concerns or physical pain, I intend for it to clear away on its own and think of it like this:

> Pain or illness is just a temporary change in my energy. If there are others who've cleared years of chronic pain or illness by guiding their thoughts, why can't I? Perhaps my body's flow of energy was blocked or became stagnant. It's just getting me to pay attention. It will leave my energy as I allow myself to feel at ease and be in joy more often. And it may even leave as soon as I take my attention away from it and focus on how I *want* to feel. My intention alone has the power to get things moving in that direction. It's safe to let it all go when I'm ready. I'm clearing space for positive energy to flow more easily to me now.

How does it feel when I've turned my focus away from any stress or previous concern for my health? What's it like when I'm free of distractions and my mind is completely free to focus on what's important to me? What would I be daydreaming about?

_____

I am now achieving an atmosphere for success in achieving an even higher level of wellbeing. *Your turn:* I am
_____.

What do you love about the direction your wellbeing is headed toward and why?

_____

_____

_____

_____

Intentions for My Day (Or tomorrow)

What words describe my day? I am feeling _____. I am being _____. I am having
_____. I am doing _____. How will I look and feel at the end of the day? Imagine it now.

It's time to honor my body's wishes more consistently. How does it feel to honor my body? How does it feel to be so tuned into my body that I know what it needs? What if I knew that following those little nudges to get up and stretch, drink more water, or breathe more deeply would prevent any further stress or pain?

What are the signs that my body has given me recently? Can I think of any right now? What are they?

_____

_____

_____

_____

_____

I intend to honor my body's requests to:

_____

_____

_____

_____

_____

To feel more at ease throughout my day, I am...

_____

_____

_____

_____

_____

If I wanted to offer words that would honor my body, what would I say? The many things that I appreciate about my body that have supported me through my life are:

_____

_____

_____

_____

If my body could speak to me, what do I think it would be telling me? I can close my eyes right now and tune in to my body and feel anywhere that may be asking for attention. Take a moment to do this now.

_____

_____

_____

_____

Since deep breathing is the first step in self-healing, take a moment to practice; begin by focusing on slowing your breath, allowing a slight pause between breaths. You may notice this clearing your thoughts. If not, try counting. Breathe in for three to four seconds, allow for a slight pause, and breathe out for four to six. After a few breaths, come back to your natural rhythm. Consider doing this daily; once in the morning, just before returning home from your day, and again before going to sleep. Practicing this will remind you to breathe more deeply throughout your day.

I am better every day at honoring my body's wishes. And I am full of energy and vitality! *Your turn*: I am

_____

How are you feeling today and why do you think that is?

*If not ideal, how do you want to feel and what are the words that would describe it?
And what else could you do today or this week that will help you feel even better?*

_____
_____
_____
_____
_____
_____
_____
_____
_____
_____
_____
_____
_____
_____
_____
_____
_____
_____
_____
_____

Intentions for My Day (Or tomorrow)

What words describe my day? I am feeling _____. I am being _____. I am having _____. I am doing _____. How will I look and feel at the end of the day? Imagine it now.

I am in charge of how I feel. I am practicing how I want to feel and repeating it over and over again until I believe it. Until I believe in me. Until I believe in my ability to be and have and do anything I wish. And I practice it *so* masterfully that I end up being able to feel good no matter what is happening around me. My thoughts, intentions, and energy are that powerful!

How do I want to feel? This week is all about practicing thoughts that allow me to align with my best possible health. I want to achieve this because wellbeing is natural to me and I deserve to feel good *all* the time.

The many ways it will benefit me are...

_____
_____
_____
_____

I am ready to let this happen because...

_____
_____
_____

Having it is making my work life easier because...

_____
_____
_____

I love how good I feel when I'm aligned with the mindset of total wellbeing because...

_____
_____
_____

What are the words or phrases that describe how it feels when my mind and body are in that state as of right now? Think of feeling your best from morning to night; at work, home, or with friends. I am full of vitality and I feel...

Now look at one word at a time that you wrote above and imagine you're breathing in the energy of what it means. As you exhale; think "I choose to feel," and as you breathe in, read the next word. Do your best to feel the emotion associated with each word and allow your body to respond.

Now close your eyes and imagine how you look and feel in that state. How much more can my physical body show me the positive results of how I'm thinking and feeling? My body is now transforming to accommodate my every wish. I am keeping the image impressed upon my mind and becoming one with its energy.

The more I practice thoughts, actions, and intentions that align with my true nature, the better I feel. And the better I feel, the more I attract more love, joy, wellbeing, and abundance into my life.

Going forward, if desired; to practice any feeling you wish to feel more often, begin asking yourself how you want to feel each day. Then think of the words that would describe it.

I am now achieving the feeling of total wellbeing. *Your turn*: I am _____.
Why is it becoming so easy for me to feel better any time I want?

Who or what are you appreciating today and why?

_____

_____

_____

_____

_____

_____

_____

_____

_____

_____

_____

_____

_____

_____

_____

_____

_____

_____

Intentions for My Day (Or tomorrow)

What words describe my day? I am feeling _____. I am being _____. I am having _____. I am doing _____. How will I look and feel at the end of the day? Imagine it now.

Day 6 _____

It's time to take the next obvious step toward my goal. What actions can I take that I believe will help me achieve better health and wellbeing? *Write a list of habits or activities that you want to start doing when you're able to. Consider letting it be something you'll enjoy doing, not something you feel that you "should" do. Don't hold back. You don't have to do it all now. If desired, include what you do now and write a start date next to anything new.*

If I had an unlimited amount of time, what would I love to do that gets my body moving, makes me smile, or just feels therapeutic or good to do? I am feeling inspired to...

Daily	Weekly	Occasionally

I am frequently finding ways to smile and laugh more by...

Going forward, I am taking the time to nurture or spoil myself more by...

_____

_____

_____

_____

_____

_____

_____

_____

Consider trying 5-15 minutes a day of meditation or a deep breathing exercise. It's potentially life-changing, as it can improve your focus, immune system, energy, and intuition on how to achieve goals, as well as speed up the manifestation of desires.

I am feeling more inspired every day to take the next step toward my goal. *Your turn*: I am _____.

Which activity is the most fun or satisfying to think about and why?
And which one(s) do you plan to do first and why?

_____

_____

_____

_____

_____

_____

_____

_____

_____

_____

_____

_____

_____

_____

_____

_____

_____

Intentions for My Day (Or tomorrow)

What words describe my day? I am feeling _____. I am being _____. I am having _____. I am doing _____. How will I look and feel at the end of the day? Imagine it now.

It's time to practice my belief and expectation of things working out for me. I choose to focus on what I want and practice believing it's who I am. All I need to do is be in the energy of it, and like a magnet, I will bring it into being. It's done. I am as aligned with wellbeing as I believe I am.

When it comes to my health, I feel good about...

_____

_____

_____

_____

I feel mentally and physically strongest when I am...

_____

_____

_____

_____

I choose to believe my body is naturally strong and resilient and is capable of...

_____

_____

_____

_____

What else do I believe is working out for me?

_____

_____

_____

_____

I expect things to continue going well for me because...

_____

_____

_____

_____

If it was happening right now and I felt how I wanted to feel and was having the kind of day I would love to have *every* day, what would I be doing right now? Where would I be? What would I be thinking about? Who would I be with? What are we talking about or planning to do? What else is happening?

_____

_____

_____

_____

_____

_____

_____

_____

_____

_____

_____

_____

I believe in my ability to achieve anything I decide to do. Blissful wellbeing is natural to me and I am now aligning with it. I am allowing myself to feel really good about where I am and excited for what's to come. I am holding the vision of it in my mind and letting go of the how, and I feel free. I am simply letting myself be in the joy of who I am. *Your turn*: I am_____.

Whether it's based on your will and determination, your belief and expectation, or the power of your mind, how much more are you able to believe in your natural ability to achieve total wellbeing? Imagine it's like being given a placebo or button to push that instantly aligns you with it. What part of this ability or your desired outcome do you believe in most and why?

_____

_____

_____

_____

_____

_____

_____

_____

_____

_____

_____

_____

_____

_____

_____

_____

Intentions for My Day (Or tomorrow)

What words describe my day? I am feeling _____. I am being _____. I am having _____. I am doing _____. How will I look and feel at the end of the day? Imagine it now.

My emotions and how I'm feeling are the result of what I'm focusing on. How does it feel to know that nothing has to be a struggle for me? If any problems arise, I focus on the solution. Sometimes that just means I look at how I want things to be, and the answers will come. The idea is to have a way to feel better any time something has the potential to take me out of my good-feeling place.

Is there anything going on currently that I wish to find a positive solution for? If desired, think of a recent situation with an individual or group, or just something that's weighing on the mind. What is it?

_____

_____

_____

I immediately focus on a solution by deciding how I want things to be. What would I rather have happen if I could replay the scene or have it turn out that way the next time it occurs, if applicable?

_____

_____

_____

_____

_____

_____

Additionally, what's another way to look at this situation that makes me feel better about it?

_____

_____

_____

_____

Is there anything I can do that will make things easier?

_____

_____

_____

How would it feel to have this situation be really comfortable for me?

_____

_____

What are the words to describe how I feel when a better outcome is taking place?

_____

_____

_____

What are the words to describe how I feel afterward?

_____

_____

_____

_____

_____

I can close my eyes right now and see my desired end result. I see everyone involved doing better and feel that it's all that I hoped it would be, or better. It feels easy. We're on the same wavelength and enjoying ourselves. If I think of this and send everyone wishes for an easier day right before I see them each time, I may be surprised at my ability to transform this situation. Any time I change how I am thinking and feeling and acting, I am changing my circumstances. That being said, if it doesn't feel good to think about this particular situation, I think of another area of my life that *does* feel good. Putting my attention on any area of my life that I feel really good about is allowing all areas of my life to become better and easier.

I am better every day at letting any struggle go and allowing myself to feel good. Anything I once thought of as a problem is an opportunity for my growth. I am focused on solutions from this point forward. *Your turn*: I am

_____.

What do you love about your current mindset in relation to your health and wellbeing and why? Or use this space to write more on this day's topic or anything you wish...

_____

_____

_____

_____

_____

_____

_____

_____

_____

_____

_____

_____

_____

Intentions for My Day (Or tomorrow)

What words describe my day? I am feeling _____. I am being _____. I am having _____. I am doing _____. How will I look and feel at the end of the day? Imagine it now. I am doing my best to speak of what I want and leave out what I don't want. So that way, I only attract what I truly want into my life, as well as allow myself to feel at ease.

I am practicing how it feels to be in the qualities and energy of my natural state of blissful wellbeing. Basically, I follow my heart's desire and do what I believe is required for me to achieve more ease, energy, clarity, and joy. It's available to me now and there's no limit to the amount of happiness and wellbeing I can achieve. Going forward, I am doing my best to practice being one with this energy. I am living and breathing it and making it mine.

What are the qualities or characteristics that I'm in or intend to be in? I can write down what first comes to mind, and then list words from A-Z that describe my mood, personality, style, or how I'm acting (smiling, laughing, charming) when I'm looking and feeling my best. *Have fun with this! If you find yourself laughing at yourself for what you wrote, even better!*

_____	_____	_____
_____	_____	_____
_____	_____	_____
_____	_____	_____
_____	_____	_____
_____	_____	_____
_____	_____	_____
_____	_____	_____
_____	_____	_____

What else am I choosing to be or have or do from this point forward? From now on, with the best of my intentions: I am choosing to feel...

_____

_____

_____

I am choosing to be...

_____

_____

_____

I am choosing to have...

_____

_____

_____

I am choosing to enjoy more...

_____

_____

_____

I am choosing to do more...

_____

_____

_____

I decided this and I intend to keep it going. It's all happening now or in the days, weeks, or months to come.

How much better or how much more blissful am I able to feel right now? *If desired, slow your breath and feel as though you're breathing in the energy of blissful wellbeing into your entire body. Close your eyes, put your attention on your heart center and ask again. Allow your body to respond.* How much more blissful am I able to feel right now? Show me how it feels.

How much more am I able to feel this way in the days ahead? When I'm feeling blissful every morning and letting it carry me through my day, what's it like to live that way? And how do I feel at the end of the day when everything's gone my way? Why is it suddenly getting easier for me to feel more comfortable in my body and joyful in my mind?

If desired, 1) Make note of anything you practiced in the past ten days that felt good to you if you would like to continue the practice. 2) Consider writing down your favorite thought-provoking question and affirmation somewhere and practice saying it every morning as soon as you wake up or throughout your day. Continue if it feels good. You will add to this list throughout the book so when you're done with it you will have practiced saying 10 affirmations. Practiced thought = belief = the feeling of it being a part of you = becomes your reality. Additionally, ask yourself daily, "How does it feel when I allow myself to feel blissful?"

I am practicing the feeling of anything I wish to achieve until I make it mine. I am taking the path to my greatest joy and wellbeing. And I know I deserve it! *Your turn*: I am_____.

You can imagine telling a friend about your success in achieving your highest level of wellbeing, see their excited response, and lock in the feeling of it. *If it feels good to think of it, recall this scene as often as you wish, and watch how much better you begin to feel. They're sitting in front of you. What are you telling them?*

_____

_____

_____

_____

_____

_____

_____

_____

_____

_____

Intentions for My Day (Or tomorrow)

What words describe my day? I am feeling _____. I am being _____. I am having _____. I am doing _____. How will I look and feel at the end of the day? Imagine it now.

More Appreciation & Intentions

Consider doing this before you go to sleep so it's the last thought on your mind to ensure better sleep, better dreams, and better outcomes. Setting frequent intentions and practicing thoughts of appreciation will attract more of what you enjoy into your life. Repetition will instill it and soon you will find yourself thinking of it without needing to remind yourself.

What was my favorite part about today or this past week? Can I recall any great conversations or laughter with family, colleagues, or friends? Am I feeling good about any goals or tasks I accomplished?

_____

_____

_____

What are three or more things I felt appreciation for and why?

_____

_____

_____

_____

_____

_____

What are some things that happened or that I did that made me feel better about myself or my health?

_____

_____

_____

I appreciate myself for how much I am choosing to feel more at ease in the following ways:
At home, I am...

_____

_____

_____

At work, I am...

_____

_____

_____

With my friends, I am...

_____

_____

_____

In my personal time, I am...

_____

_____

_____

I will always do my best to feel happy where I am and excited for what's to come. Right now I am reaching for thoughts of appreciation about anything in my life that makes me feel fortunate to be who I am. I am living a life I love more every day. With my life in general, I feel _really_ good about...

_____

_____

_____

_____

Every day I get better at...

_____

Intentions for the Days Ahead

What's my intention for this coming week or so? How do I expect things to go? What are all the words or phrases that describe my week and how do I feel at the end of the week? If there's anything I wish to accomplish, what is it and how does it feel to have it done?

_____

_____

_____

_____

_____

_____

_____

_____

Now, close your eyes and take about thirty seconds to visualize it the way you want it to be. Then see tomorrow go as you expect it to, from morning to night. See a smile on your face at the end of the day, knowing that you accomplished what you set out to do and felt great all day. If desired, visualize your day before you fall asleep each night. See it and feel the ease of it. You may be surprised at the results. It will happen as I expect it to, or better.

The deeper I breathe, the stronger my immune system may be and the more lasting my energy can be. What are the words that will inspire me to check in throughout my day and remind me to breathe more deeply?

_____

_____

★ _First thing in the morning, before you get out of bed or when you first look in the mirror, always ask yourself:_ "How do I wish to feel throughout my day today? I choose to feel _____."

For the next ten days, the topic will mainly be on what you wrote on Day 1 as your desired end result for...

My Mind is: _____. Please fill it in once again. Now imagine you're speaking directly to your desire. Tell it specifically how you want it to *think* and how you want it to make you *feel* and why.

Dear Mind,

_____

_____

_____

_____

_____

_____

_____

_____

_____

Additionally, I want a clearer mind so that I can...

_____

_____

_____

I want to be more focused so that I can...

_____

_____

_____

I want to be more decisive about...

_____

_____

_____

I want to feel mentally strong when I...

_____

_____

_____

I want to let go of self-doubting thoughts and have more confidence about...

_____

_____

_____

I want to feel more present so that I can notice...

_____

_____

_____

I also want a clearer mind so that I can spend more time thinking about...

_____

_____

_____

I want to think less about...

_____

_____

_____

I believe I can do all of this one day at a time, and I love letting it be easy for me. If I could speak to the desire for the *ease* of achieving this ideal state of mind, I would say I love having this come easily to me because...

_____

_____

I'm so thankful that I'm allowing this to happen because I deserve to feel good and live my best life. Thank you, mind, for the clarity and peace, and for working with my body in harmonious ways. I am full of clarity and harmony. *Your turn*: I am _____.

Write more on this topic or anything you wish

_____

_____

_____

_____

_____

_____

_____

_____

_____

_____

Intentions for My Day (Or tomorrow)

What words describe my day? I am feeling _____. I am being _____. I am having _____. I am doing _____. How will I look and feel at the end of the day? Imagine it now.

I like knowing that I can just focus on what I want and how I want to feel, and let go of how it will happen. The answers will come as I allow myself to relax and go with the flow more. I'm just practicing it more consistently until I can feel how I want to feel all day, every day.

This is where I describe how my life is when I'm full of clarity or anything else I choose for my mindset and how I want to feel. How am I *thinking* and *acting* and *feeling* when I'm there?

I am spending more time thinking about...

_____

_____

Emotionally, I am feeling...

_____

_____

Physically, I am feeling...

_____

_____

I am feeling more confident about...

_____

_____

I am feeling more connected to myself because...

_____

_____

I am being more mindful about...

_____

_____

I am having more fun doing...

_____

_____

I am doing more of what I wish to do for my peace of mind. I am...

_____

_____

My life feels better because I am...

_____

_____

Additionally, my life has changed in the following ways:

_____

_____

_____

If my intuition or inner guidance could speak to me, what words of encouragement would it give me in regards to letting myself off the hook more often and just letting myself be in the joy of who I am?

_____

_____

_____

_____

_____

What would it tell you it needs from you right now? Close your eyes a moment and tune into what feels like the center of your mind. See if you can sense anything it's asking for. Write down anything that first comes to mind. This may feel like your imagination, but is often your natural intuition.

_____

_____

_____

_____

As I tune into myself more frequently and let my intentions be known, I am allowing my mind, body, and spirit to work together in harmony and assist me in achieving my goals. And do you know why things are easier for me now? I am following my heart and making my choices based on what feels right to me.

My life has changed because of it. My favorite part about it is...

_____

I am now aligning with the energy of clarity. *Your turn*: I am _____.

✱ ✳ ✱ ✳ ✱ ✳ ✱ ✳ ✱ ✳ ✱ ✳ ✱ ✳ ✱ ✳ ✱ ✳ ✱

What part of your current state of mind do you love most and why?

_____

_____

_____

_____

_____

_____

Intentions for My Day (Or tomorrow)

What words describe my day? I am feeling _____. I am being _____. I am having _____. I am doing _____. How will I look and feel at the end of the day? Imagine it now.

Now that I've decided what I want and what it's like to have it, I am creating an atmosphere for success for gaining more clarity and peace of mind or anything else I wish for my mental wellbeing. What can I do to set myself up for success in continuing with my healthiest mindset? Are there any changes that need to be made to my current atmosphere, physical or otherwise?

Let's begin by checking in and making peace with where I am. What is going really well in relation to my level of clarity or the wellbeing of my mind?

_____

_____

I feel the most clear-minded when I am spending time doing...

_____

_____

I feel more focused while getting tasks or errands done when I am...

_____

_____

I feel the most present when I am...

_____

_____

I feel the most calm or peaceful when I am...

_____

_____

I feel the most joyful when I am...

_____

_____

What's not feeling right? If I had a magic wand, what changes would I make, if any? (*The magic is in believing you can have it any way you want it to be, or better. That goes for everything. It begins with a decision. I decide. I get to choose. I make the rules. I am in charge. Ta-da!*).

_____

The habits or activities I enjoy that support my desire for more clarity and I plan to continue are...

_____

_____

The habits or activities that are not feeling right and I prefer to stop doing once I'm feeling ready are...

_____

_____

What does having more clarity mean to me?

_____

_____

How would this change my life?

_____

I believe it's achievable because...

_____

What needs to happen in order for me to make it available to me right now? What state of mind do I think I need to be in to achieve it?

_____

_____

_____

If my intuition or inner guidance could speak to me, what do I think it would tell me to do differently at home, at work, or in my personal life, if anything? What would support my wellbeing? Take a moment to close your eyes and think of this now. Your natural intuition will give you a positive message, so let go of anything that feels like you "should" do it.

_____

_____

What would it tell me to do additionally, during my morning or evening routine? And what about my bedtime or sleep routine?

_____

_____

How much more clarity am I able to have right now? Today and in the days ahead, I am achieving an atmosphere for success in gaining more clarity. *Your turn:* I am _____.

What do you love about the direction your mindset is headed and why?

_____

_____

_____

_____

_____

Intentions for My Day (Or tomorrow)

What words describe my day? I am feeling _____. I am being _____. I am having _____. I am doing _____. How will I look and feel at the end of the day? Imagine it now.

Everything in life can be easy. It's not meant to be hard. And I like knowing that my life can be easy if I let it be. Sometimes it's just about letting go of the unwanted and giving all my attention to what I want. And even though I would love to jump right in and start practicing more positive thoughts, I know how beneficial it can be to acknowledge and intend to release any limiting thoughts or beliefs that I may have. In a way it's like saying goodbye to them.

The moment I start to let go of negative emotion is the moment I begin to align more fully with *all* my desires. My mind becomes clear. My body heals and reaches its highest level of wellbeing. I'm able to reach my potential in all areas of my life, and my wishes begin to manifest more easily.

Let's just say I'm in charge of how my life goes. If I know my thoughts create my reality, what thoughts do I want to clear and which thoughts do I want to keep?

Slowly read through these questions and feel the effects of these potential changes and what's available to you:

How does it feel to give myself permission to feel good?
How does it feel to make peace with what has been?
How does it feel to truly appreciate where I am?
How does it feel to be free of any constraints or struggle?
How does it feel to have more energy to do what I love to do?
How does it feel to free up my mind to create more blissful thoughts?
How does it feel to allow myself to focus on the joy in my life and let go of anything else?
How does it feel to position myself for better things to come?

I want to let go of any struggle, such as worries, fears, guilt, or resentment, because I would rather spend my time thinking about...

_____

_____

When I'm ready, I am making peace with myself and what was. For anything that's been before, it brought me to where I am now. And I feel *so* very fortunate to be who I am.

A little homework for you - if you're comfortable with it, write down anything you wish to release or let go of on a separate piece of paper. Don't hold back; you're going to rip it up and throw it away afterward. First consider how it feels to give yourself permission to let go of anything that's been weighing on your mind. What if you could wipe the slate clean and start over? You can. Really!

Grab your pen and paper and make your list; include anything you can think of that you wish to let go of (repetitive thoughts, situations, beliefs, habits, etc.). Then state your intention to release and let go of it. Here's an example but feel free to make up your own:

I am deciding right now to acknowledge and release any habits, thoughts, beliefs, or lower energy that no longer serve me. I'm making peace with myself and my past, and it's clearing my mind. In this moment or in the days or weeks ahead, any concerns or negative emotions about this will leave me and any issues associated with them are being resolved. I give myself permission to let go of it as I become ready, and know that it's safe to do so. My positive thoughts and energy will transform these old beliefs without any further effort on my part.

I am being gentle and easy about it, and it will fall away on its own. I release all of this, and I am free.

Review your list one more time if you'd like. And then draw a big smiley face and rip it up to bits. Intend to call back all of your energy now.

What are the words that describe how it feels to be free from any struggle or hindering thoughts or beliefs I may have had? How does it feel when I allow my mind to feel open, spacious, and full of clarity? What does that feel like? Close your eyes and take yourself there now. What's it like?

_____

_____

_____

In what ways do I believe letting go of these concerns will change my life? What will I do with the extra time I have?

_____

_____

Take a moment to close your eyes and slowly repeat the words "I am full of clarity and my mind is clear; clear and spacious, clear and spacious, clear and spacious."

As I release or transform anything unwanted, I'm raising my vibrational energy and will align more easily with my highest level of wellbeing. I'll look back one day and realize that I stopped thinking about that thing that seemed to linger on my mind for so long. And then I'll realize I'm also not continuing old patterns or situations that seemed to repeat themselves before. They only came up because I gave them my attention. It feels so good to notice when these positive changes occur!

My path is clear and I'm on my way to more joy. I am better every day at tuning in to the inner peace that's available to me. I am full of peace and clarity. And I love knowing that I am in a constant state of change and becoming better every day in every way. *Your turn*: I am _____.

How are you feeling today and why do you think that is?
If you think you could feel even better, what are the words that would describe it?
Breathe in the meaning or energy of each word as it's written.

_____

_____

_____

_____

_____

_____

Intentions for My Day (Or tomorrow)

What words describe my day? I am feeling _____. I am being _____. I am having _____. I am doing _____. How will I look and feel at the end of the day? Imagine it now.

I'm in charge of how I feel. How do I want to feel? This week is all about allowing myself to feel more present and have more peace of mind and clarity. I want this because it will feel so good. I am ready to let this happen because...

_____

_____

How does it feel to have more clarity? What does having more clarity allow me to do better in my life?

_____

_____

_____

_____

_____

_____

How does it feel to be so clear on who I am and what I want, that I know what my next step is? What could that step be?

_____

One way to clear a cluttered mind is to take time to relax or have fun and get my mind off whatever is on my mind. What is my favorite thing to do that helps me relax or forget my worries?

_____

What are some things that thrill me to think about that can replace any unwanted thoughts the next time they clutter my mind, if ever?

_____

What am I paying attention to throughout my typical day or week? If I'm ever focused on things that bother me, what else is happening that feels good to me?

_____

_____

_____

_____

What are some ways I can practice purposely noticing all the positive things that go on around me and let go of anything else?

_____

_____

_____

From now on I'm going to do my best to focus on what I want. If not already, I am practicing until it's natural to me and the clarity keeps flowing. My mind is free and clear. This is the ultimate good-feeling place to be.

How does it feel when I'm full of clarity? What are the words that would describe how I feel, what I'm doing differently, or how my day goes at home or work? What do I believe is improving when I have even more clarity than I have now?

_____

_____

_____

_____

_____

What are some more words that will guide me there? I can guide my mind and body to align with my desires.

Mind, it's time to focus. It's time to set aside my repetitive thoughts. Show me how it feels to have clarity. How does it *feel* when I allow clarity to flow? How does it feel when I *allow* my mind to clear? Can I feel my mind creating space? How spacious is it? Is it clearing now or more so in the minutes to follow? Is my breath slowing down and becoming deeper? How will it feel when I allow myself to have clarity all day? I have the feeling that my day's going to go easier. I am going to be sharper. I am at an all-new level of clarity.

Your turn: I am _____.
The easiest way to practice feeling how you want to feel may be just closing your eyes and thinking of as many words as you can think of that describe how you're wanting to feel in that moment. If not now, with practice you will be able to intend this and feel an immediate shift of your energy, and clarity can come instantly.

What is your favorite part about having more clarity or a peaceful mind and why?

_____

_____

_____

_____

_____

_____

_____

_____

_____

_____

_____

_____

_____

Intentions for My Day (Or tomorrow)

What words describe my day? I am feeling _____. I am being _____. I am having _____. I am doing _____. How will I look and feel at the end of the day? Imagine it now.

It's time to take the next obvious step toward my goal. What actions can I take that I believe will help me achieve more mindfulness and clarity? What would help me release resistance or struggle, if any? How does it feel to have a peaceful mind, easily focus on any task, and feel more joyful and present? Not to mention a higher state of wellbeing? I love knowing I can do all of this in just a few minutes a day with deep breathing or meditation.

Another way to relieve my mind is to write down anything that I can't seem to stop thinking about. Whether it's a plan to get things done or just let it go until I have time for it, it feels great to record it and free up my mind.

If I could let go of this *one* thing, I would have more peace of mind. What is it?

_____

If I let go of *this* one thing, I could focus more easily on any task. What is it?

_____

If my intuition could speak to me right now, it would tell me to let go of...

_____

It's been nudging me to stop doing...

_____

It's been nudging me to keep doing...

_____

It's been nudging me to start doing...

_____

Are these thoughts coming from my natural inner guidance/intuition? Does it feel good to think of it? Is it how I truly feel, or is there a fear or guilt behind these thoughts, which are generally not based on my own beliefs in the first place? *Review them once again and determine what feels like it's aligned with your true nature.*

If it feels good, I can also decide to only surround myself with things that bring me joy and discard or give away anything else. Without any guilt, self-judgment, or what I think I'm "supposed" to do, consider what feels good to let go of.

Now for the simple pleasure of getting it off your mind, write a list of things you've been wanting to do or need to do or may want to let go of. This can be for anything you repeatedly remind yourself to do. There's no need to take action on any of this until you feel like it, if ever. Clearing physical clutter and need-to-do's is known to open up doors for new opportunities and lucrative projects for individuals and companies. For decluttering material things, ask yourself if you have used it in a year or so, need it or love it, or enjoy it.

To-Do	To Stop Doing	Discard	To Donate	To Store Away
_____	_____	_____	_____	_____
_____	_____	_____	_____	_____
_____	_____	_____	_____	_____
_____	_____	_____	_____	_____

_____   _____   _____   _____   _____
_____   _____   _____   _____   _____
_____   _____   _____   _____   _____
_____   _____   _____   _____   _____
_____   _____   _____   _____   _____
_____   _____   _____   _____   _____
_____   _____   _____   _____   _____
_____   _____   _____   _____   _____
_____   _____   _____   _____   _____
_____   _____   _____   _____   _____
_____   _____   _____   _____   _____

If you happen to like the idea of acting on this, consider circling those you'd like to do first and schedule 15-30 minutes every two weeks or so, set a timer, and begin with one email, phone call, or one drawer or closet. Then enjoy the positive momentum and influx of new ideas that come as a result of decluttering.

And now for easier decision-making, is there anything that I am feeling stuck on or needing to make a decision on now or in the near future? *If choices are involved, write down the entire scenario if you were to choose each path. Then read them one at a time, close your eyes and imagine what it's like once it has taken place. Decide which one feels better or has the least resistance and include doing nothing if that's an option.*

Choice 1	Choice 2	Choice 3
_____	_____	_____
_____	_____	_____
_____	_____	_____
_____	_____	_____
_____	_____	_____
_____	_____	_____

The choice is right for me if it feels good, easy, or exciting. I'm not questioning it. I'm all in. I know that it's what I want. If I'm questioning a choice I'm making, it's time to take a step back and get some clarity. When making the best choice for me, I'll never need to rationalize anything.

I am creating space for inner peace and positive change. I am more inspired every day to take the next step toward my goal for mindfulness and clarity. *Your turn:* I am_____.
Why is it so easy for me to allow my mind to feel a little freer now?

Intentions for My Day (Or tomorrow)

What words describe my day? I am feeling _____. I am being _____. I am having _____. I am doing _____. How will I look and feel at the end of the day? Imagine it now.

Does it sometimes feel as though there's so much to do and so much on my mind, that I'm not letting myself be present? As though there's not enough time for it? What if I could practice being more present in my life just by reminding myself that right now is all that matters? Right now is the moment that counts. Right now is where I set my intentions. This is where my power lies. And how I'm feeling right now is setting the tone for what happens next. If I had an unlimited amount of time, what would I be doing differently? If I can believe and expect that I have time to be more present, I can create that for myself. I'm creating it right now.

I'm stepping into a place where I've just been given an *endless* slot of time where I can do whatever I want. What are the moments of my typical day that I would choose to be more present for, and why?

_____
_____
_____
_____
_____

What have I been wanting to have more time for? *Write a list of things you would be doing with this free time.* I have time for...

_____   _____   _____
_____   _____   _____
_____   _____   _____
_____   _____   _____
_____   _____   _____
_____   _____   _____
_____   _____   _____
_____   _____   _____

How does it *feel* to have all this free time, and to be doing more of what I want to do?

_____
_____
_____
_____

My desire for this has set things in motion, and circumstances are now being shifted around for it to come about. My expectation of it is creating an unexpected amount of extra time for me to enjoy.

If feeling as though I have more time to spare is helping me be more present throughout my day, how is this improving my life? What's it like to be free of distraction and feel very content with where I am in the moment?

_____
_____
_____
_____

And how does it feel to be so present that I feel able to breathe with ease and be in a state of peace and joy no matter where I am? I can close my eyes and imagine I'm in my favorite place to be. How does it feel to be completely present and have so much appreciation for what I see and hear and feel? Imagine this now.

What do I love about this moment I'm in *right now*?

_____

What does feeling mindfully present mean to me when I'm fully aware of the sights and sounds around me?

_____

What does being present mean to me in the moments that I tune into myself and become aware of my body or breath or deepest desires? What's it like to do that right now? How did it feel?

_____

What does being present mean to me when I'm focused on a task at home or work or in a conversation? What can I do to be more present at these times, and how does it improve matters?

_____

_____

The times I cherish most are often those that I find myself being completely in the joy of the moment. This happens most often when...

_____

_____

_____

I cherish my life and believe in giving myself the life I deserve. A life where I have time to do what's important to me. What lights me up, makes me happy, makes me laugh, and makes me appreciate the life I have? That's what I'm going to do from now on. Yes, yes, yes! I am.

As I become more mindful and connected to the present moment, I am creating a stronger connection with myself. I am making myself and how I feel more important than anything else, and I so deserve it! I am now forming the habit of being more present wherever I go. *Your turn*: I am _____.

How much more are you able to believe in your ability to achieve more clarity and feel more present or anything else you desire for your state of mind?
What part of your desired outcome do you believe in most and why?

_____

_____

_____

Intentions for My Day (Or tomorrow)

What words describe my day? I am feeling _____. I am being _____. I am having _____. I am doing _____. How will I look and feel at the end of the day? Imagine it now. Consider taking on a new habit of asking yourself, "What do I love about this moment?"

This is our day for positive solutions. The goal this week is to practice allowing myself to have more peace of mind. When I have an uncomfortable thought or memory come up frequently or occasionally, I can replace it with something I prefer to think of and give it a new meaning. In time, the other thought pattern can be left behind. It can be helpful to communicate this desired change to my mind. I can do this by intending to erase or black out the image, or just say "release it, thank you" any time something unwanted comes up. Then follow it immediately with a word or image I intend to replace it with. I can think of a word or phrase that resonates for me that will redirect that thought. Such as release, peace, freedom, harmony, or a phrase like "I choose wellbeing." It could even be a  smiley face or favorite symbol. And the moment I think of it I'm deciding to breathe in the energy of that word or symbol and let go of the thought I had. For even better results, I can take it a step further by thinking of a tranquil or happy scene. It could be my favorite place or somewhere I'd like to go. *See yourself in the picture or feel that you're there. Now it's time to create your plan for replacing any unwanted thoughts, in much detail.*

My chosen word or phrase is _____.

To me, the meaning of this word is all about…

_____

_____

_____

_____

This is how it feels in my body…

_____

_____

_____

_____

_____

_____

_____

Here's a description of my ideal tranquil or fun scene that takes me right to that good-feeling place, like I'm on vacation. It reminds me that I'd rather spend every minute of my precious life thinking about all the joy and possibilities available to me than anything else. I can feel like this every day! When I'm there, what do I see in front of me? What's behind me and all around me? What am I doing? Who am I with? What's the look on my face?

_____

_____

_____

_____

_____

_____

When I'm in this ideal place, I am feeling...

_____

_____

_____

_____

Take a moment to close your eyes and think of how it would feel to actually be there. Then say your word to lock it in to your memory. If not now, with practice, the word or image will allow your mind and body to recall this feeling.

Ideally: Catch yourself having the thought ~ think "release it, thank you" or exhale it out with your intention ~ say or think of your word/symbol ~ breathe in ~ picture the scene = Inner Peace ☺

Whatever that thought was isn't anything worth taking myself out of a good-feeling place. This is my intention statement for how I would like things to go any time an uncomfortable thought or memory comes up, if at all...

_____

_____

_____

_____

I'm in charge. I make the rules. I get to decide. I am the master of my mind. I am taking charge of how I think and feel and re-programming old thought patterns. I am creating new thought patterns and beliefs that are creating new neural pathways. This gives me the ability to transform my life in whatever way I choose. But all I really need to do is allow myself to feel good as often as I can. My life is unfolding perfectly.

I maintain balance as I am breathing in peace and breathing out any tension. I am better every day at guiding my thoughts to a better-feeling place. _Your turn_: I am _____.

What do you love about your current state of mind and ability to stay in a good-feeling place and why?

_____

_____

_____

_____

_____

_____

_____

Intentions for My Day (Or tomorrow)

What words describe my day? I am feeling _____. I am being _____. I am having _____. I am doing _____. How will I look and feel at the end of the day? Imagine it now.

What are the qualities, energy, or mindset that I'm in or intend to be in to align with more clarity and easy, peaceful circumstances? Write down what first comes to mind. If desired, think of words or phrases that begin with letters A-Z . How am I acting or feeling in each area of my life when I'm full of clarity and have more peace in my life? I am...

_____   _____   _____
_____   _____   _____
_____   _____   _____
_____   _____   _____
_____   _____   _____
_____   _____   _____
_____   _____   _____
_____   _____   _____
_____   _____   _____
_____   _____   _____
_____   _____   _____
_____   _____   _____
_____   _____   _____

What else am I choosing to be or have or do from this point forward? From now on, with the best of my intentions: I am choosing to feel...

_____
_____
_____

I am choosing to be more...

_____
_____
_____

I am choosing to have more...

_____
_____
_____

I am choosing to enjoy more...

_____
_____
_____

To feel more mindful throughout my day, I am...

_____

_____

_____

How much more peace of mind am I able to feel right now? *If desired, slow your breath and feel as though you're breathing in the energy of peace into your entire body. Close your eyes, put your attention on your heart center and ask again.* How much more inner peace am I able to feel right now? Body, show me how it feels.

How much more am I able to feel this way in the days ahead? Why is it suddenly so easy for me to have more peace in my heart and clarity of mind? What's it like to have a clear, open, and receptive mind and feel the whole meaning of clarity? How would this improve my days in the weeks ahead?

_____

_____

_____

If desired, 1) Make note of anything you practiced in the past ten days that felt good to you and you wish to continue. 2) Add your favorite thought-provoking question and affirmation to the list you started.

If I'm wanting more peace, I'm going to create it wherever I go. I am as peaceful as I let myself be. And I am full of clarity! I am now achieving the mindset that is supporting my desire for total wellbeing. *Your turn*: I am

_____.

Imagine telling someone about a new, peaceful, easy feeling you've been having lately that seems to last throughout your day. What would you say about it?

_____

_____

_____

_____

_____

_____

_____

_____

_____

_____

_____

_____

Intentions for My Day (Or tomorrow)

What words describe my day? I am feeling _____. I am being _____. I am having _____. I am doing _____. How will I look and feel at the end of the day? Imagine it now.

More Appreciation & Intentions

What was my favorite part about today or this past week?

_____

_____

What are three or more things I felt appreciation for and why?

_____

_____

_____

_____

_____

What are some things that happened or that I did that made me feel better about myself or gave me more clarity or peace of mind?

_____

_____

_____

_____

_____

I appreciate myself for how much I am choosing to feel good and be more present in the following ways:
At home, I am...

_____

_____

At work, I am...

_____

_____

With my friends, I am...

_____

_____

In my personal time, I am...

_____

_____

Every day I get better at...

_____

_____

If anything was on my mind more than I'd like, what can I appreciate about it? Is it helping me understand something better or helping me know what I don't want? What is the opposite thought, or how do I want things to be, if applicable? *If desired, play it out in your mind and see a peaceful resolution.* How would I describe it?

_____

_____

_____

Is there anyone or anything I would like to show my appreciation for today? Has anyone in particular made my day or made my week, or made things easier for me in some way? I can imagine they're in front of me right now. What would I say to them?

_____

_____

If desired, send out thoughts of appreciation and well wishes for more joy and wellbeing to anyone that comes to mind, including you!

Intentions for the Days Ahead

What's my intention for this coming week or so? How do I expect things to go? What are all the words or phrases that describe it and how do I feel at the end of the week? If there's anything I wish to accomplish at home or elsewhere, what is it and how does it feel to have it done?

_____

_____

_____

_____

_____

What am I choosing to be my defining qualities?

_____

What are the words that will inspire me to check in throughout my day and notice if or when I'm being mindful or present?

_____

_____

What am I hoping will bring me more joy this coming week? I am looking forward to...

_____

_____

Now, close your eyes and take about thirty seconds to visualize the way you want your week to go. Then see tomorrow go as you expect it to, from morning to night.

★ *First thing in the morning, ask yourself:* "How do I wish to feel throughout my day today? I choose to feel _____." If I'm looking to gain more clarity in the days ahead, I'm going to create more and more ease in my mind. I'm going to be in the joy of the moment. *It will happen as I expect it to, or better.*

A WISH Moment for Inspiration
Words Inspire Spiritual Harmony

There's always a way to feel more ease than you feel at any given moment. You may not even realize that you have any tension in your body until you try to relax different parts of the body.

You may feel the effects of this by simply reading it, but I suggest you take a moment to get into a completely comfortable position sitting or lying down, then close your eyes and take your time to guide yourself through these steps. Or even better: record yourself giving the instructions on your phone's voice memo or other mode, and play it back. Now read or record this very slowly:

Body, it's time to relax and feel completely at ease. How does it feel to allow myself to feel ease in my body?
How does it feel to allow myself to release *all* resistance?
How does it feel to be *so* relaxed that *every* muscle and *every* part of me is softer?
As I go from head to toe, I breathe in and focus on every part of me and soften any tension there.
Putting my attention on my face, breathing into it, I feel it getting softer.
Even...softer.
My forehead is softer. The layers beneath it are softer.
Even...softer.
My jaw is completely relaxed.
My neck and shoulders now...completely letting go.
Even...softer.
My arms and my hands are relaxed.
My chest feels soft inside and out.
Even...softer.
My abdomen is letting go and feeling ease.
My upper, middle, and lower back is softening right now.
Even...softer.
My hips are releasing all tension.
And now my legs are feeling completely relaxed.
Breathing into my feet, I can almost feel tingling in my toes as I take my attention there.
My body is capable of more ease. Body, double my ease...
And right now, how much more harmony can I feel in my body and my breath? Show me how it feels.
Can I feel my breath getting lighter and my body becoming even softer? How much more can I feel it?
In my next breath...I'm breathing in golden light that's doubling my energy.
How does it feel when I allow myself to feel twice as much energy?
How much more of it can I breathe into every cell of my body?
I am now refreshed and energized, and I intend to allow this feeling to stay with me the remainder of this day.

Take your time and give your body the chance to respond. Notice if you feel a change in your energy or feel relief. If not now, you will! Just practice guiding your thoughts in this way and enjoy giving yourself attention!

If not already, have faith that there will come a day when it's always possible for you to feel at ease no matter what's happening around you. If or when you encounter stressful moments, let it become your new habit to breathe in the essence of any calming word that has meaning for you. It could be ease, peace, calm, wellbeing, or anything that feels good to you.

★ I Am More Aligned With Blissful Wellbeing Every Day

Day 21 _____

For the next ten days, the topic will mainly be on what you wrote on Day 1 as your desired end result for...

My Body looks and feels: _____. Please fill it in once again.

I'm determined to have a clearer mind and a body that always feels comfortable. Essentially, I want to feel so good that I easily align with a state of blissful wellbeing. I know it's achievable, so I want to do what I can to create the best environment for that to happen, mentally *and* physically. *Imagine you're having a conversation with yourself or with a symbol that represents how you want your body to look and feel. Tell it what you want, why you want it, and what you appreciate about having it.*

Dear Body,

_____

_____

_____

_____

_____

_____

_____

_____

_____

_____

_____

_____

_____

_____

_____

_____

_____

_____

_____

_____

_____

_____

_____

_____

_____

_____

_____

Additionally, I want a completely comfortable body so that I can...

_____

_____

I also want to be more at ease so that I can focus on...

_____

I want more energy so that I can...

_____

My body deserves to feel...

_____

_____

_____

If my body could speak to me right now, what do I think it might say? What words of encouragement would it give me?

_____

_____

_____

_____

_____

What would it tell me it needs from me right now? *Close your eyes a moment and tune into your body. See if you can sense anything it's asking for. Write down anything that first comes to mind. This may feel like your imagination, but is often your intuition.*

_____

_____

_____

_____

_____

_____

_____

Thank you, my body and cells, for the wellbeing and for helping me achieve an even higher level of wellbeing. My body is responding to my thoughts. I am now aligning with the energy of a good-feeling body. *Your turn*: I am _____.

Intentions for My Day (Or tomorrow)

What words describe my day? I am feeling _____. I am being _____. I am having _____. I am doing _____. How will I look and feel at the end of the day? Imagine it now.

It's important to accept and appreciate myself and my body as I am, while keeping in mind that I am in a constant state of change and becoming who I am. My body is in the process of transforming to accommodate my wishes. My belief and expectation and trust in this is making it so. Once I've achieved this, what am I doing differently? How do I think I would be acting and feeling? *Tell your body what it will be like when you have it look and feel the way you want it to, and how it will change your life.*

_____
_____
_____
_____
_____
_____
_____
_____
_____
_____
_____
_____
_____
_____
_____
_____
_____
_____
_____
_____

Additionally, I am spending more time thinking about...

_____

Emotionally, I am feeling...

_____

Physically, I am feeling...

_____

I am feeling more confident about...

_____

I am feeling more connected to myself because...

_____

I am being...

_____

I am having more fun doing...

_____

I am doing more of what I wish to do. I am...

_____

My life feels better because I am...

_____

I am now aligning with the energy of a good-feeling body. *Your turn*: I am _____.

What qualities do you love most about yourself and your body right now, and why?

_____
_____
_____
_____
_____
_____
_____
_____
_____
_____
_____
_____
_____
_____
_____
_____
_____
_____

Intentions for My Day (Or tomorrow)

What words describe my day? I am feeling _____. I am being _____. I am having _____. I am doing _____. How will I look and feel at the end of the day? Imagine it now.

Day 23 _____

I am creating an atmosphere for success to allow my body to look and feel how I want it to.

What is going well for me now?

_____

_____

My greatest achievements or strengths in relation to my body are...

_____

_____

The habits or activities I enjoy that support my body and I plan to continue are...

_____

_____

The habits or activities that are not feeling right and I prefer to stop doing once I'm feeling ready are...

_____

_____

What do I think my body would tell me to do? Without any guilt, self-judgment, or what I think I'm "supposed" to do, what feels good to stop or start doing? What ideas or encouragement would it give me?

_____

_____

I feel best about my body when I am...

_____

_____

I am feeling really comfortable in my own skin when I am...

_____

_____

I am the most confident in how I look when...

_____

_____

I feel the most energetic when I am...

_____

I wish to improve on...

_____

_____

Is there anything that I believe is in the way of achieving my goal?

I am deciding right now that nothing is in the way. I can feel my way into any state of mind that allows me to achieve every wish, every dream, every whim. I am abundant in nature and all good things are flowing my way. Yes, please, and thank you!

What do I think it would take for me to accept myself or feel satisfied with where I am?

_____

_____

If I had a magic wand, what changes would I make to my body in relation to my wellbeing?

_____

_____

_____

How would this change my life?

_____

_____

What state of mind do I think I need to be in to achieve this? What are some new thoughts I could practice to align with the energy of my ideal body? Just for fun, let's say I pulled out my magic wand again, and it's how I want it to be. How am I feeling?

_____

_____

_____

What is an affirmation that will help me believe it's achievable?

_____

Today and in the days ahead, I am achieving an atmosphere for success in cultivating more energy and having an even better-feeling body. *Your turn*: I am _____.

What do you love about the direction you or your body is headed in and why?

_____

_____

_____

_____

_____

Intentions for My Day (Or tomorrow)

What words describe my day? I am feeling _____. I am being _____. I am having _____. I am doing _____. How will I look and feel at the end of the day? Imagine it now.

How much better am I able to feel? What do I think my body is needing from me to feel its *best*, if anything?

_____

_____

_____

What would I say is my energy level from 1-10, 10 being the highest where I feel able to enjoy doing everything I want to do on a daily basis? How much more energy would I like to have, if desired?

_____

_____

What do I love about having boundless energy and what more would I be doing?

_____

_____

_____

_____

_____

_____

_____

How satisfied am I with my sleep right now?

_____

How do I want my sleep to feel from this point forward, including how much more relaxed I feel when I'm *falling* asleep, and how much more energetic and blissful I feel when I wake up?

_____

_____

_____

_____

What do I love about sleeping so restfully that I feel energized and eager to get up in the morning?

_____

_____

_____

_____

What do I love about waking up feeling as wonderful as I'd like to and having my day go just as well?

_____

_____

_____

_____

Each night when I'm about to go to sleep, I can think about how my body will be rebuilt with perfectly healthy cells while I'm resting. Thoughts of perfect wellbeing will cause greater functioning of my body, and over time it will show me the results. When I get good and comfortable, if desired, I can place my hands over my chest (*thymus point; good for immune system/emotional balance*), right palm first. And then focus on slowing my breath, allowing a slight pause between breaths, with the exhale a bit longer than my inhale.

And then say something like this, if desired: Body and mind, it's time to relax. How does it feel when I allow myself to relax and sleep restfully? How does it feel to wake up feeling blissful? Show me how it feels. *Now, close your eyes and imagine your night's sleep and your day going as wonderfully as you'd like it to.*

If there's something else I would like help with, what is my intuition telling me? *Take a moment now and tune in to your body and sense what it may need, if anything.* What comes to mind?

_____

_____

_____

_____

_____

_____

_____

I am able to sleep as well as I wish to and have as much energy as I want! I am sleeping more restfully every night and waking up with abundant energy every morning. It just keeps getting better. *Your turn*: I am

_____.

How are you feeling today and why do you think that is?
If you think you could feel even better, what are the words that would describe it?
Breathe in the meaning of each word as it's written.

_____

_____

_____

_____

_____

_____

_____

_____

_____

Intentions for My Day (Or tomorrow)

What words describe my day? I am feeling _____. I am being _____. I am having _____. I am doing _____. How will I look and feel at the end of the day? Imagine it now.

This week is all about allowing myself to align with the energy of my best-feeling body until it's a part of who I am. Once again, it's time to practice the feeling of it. How does it feel when I allow myself to align with more ease and energy in my body, or anything else I want?

The many ways it will benefit me are...

_____
_____
_____
_____
_____

I am ready to let this happen because...

_____
_____

This is making my home and work life easier by...

_____
_____
_____
_____

I love how good I feel when I'm aligned with my natural state of wellbeing and a good-feeling body because I deserve to feel good and...

_____
_____
_____
_____

What if I started breathing slowly and deeply often enough to maintain my highest energy? Can I see myself taking the time to stop a few times throughout my day to do this? When are the best times for me to practice this?

_____

This habit of occasional slower, deeper breathing is creating a habit that lasts a lifetime and has the potential to substantially improve my emotional and physical wellbeing. The more I practice, the more natural it becomes.

My body would say I'm doing really well at being, having, or doing...

_____
_____
_____
_____

_____

_____

How does it feel to have *inexhaustible* energy all day long? I am confidently going through my day with effortless ease and abundant energy. In the days ahead, I intend to feel...

_____   _____   _____

_____   _____   _____

_____   _____   _____

_____   _____   _____

_____   _____   _____

Now one word at a time, look at anything you wrote above that describes a positive emotion (or choose new ones) and imagine you're breathing in the energy of what it means. As you exhale; think "I choose to feel," and as you breathe in, say or think of the word. Do your best to feel the emotion associated with it. Let it be your intention to feel this way today and every day. Some favorites; ease, harmony, peace, love, bliss, and free.

How much more at ease am I able to feel right now? How much more harmony can I let myself feel? How much more harmony am I able to feel in my body and my breath? *Ask the last question again with your eyes closed and take a moment to feel how your body responds. Now close your eyes and imagine how you look and feel in your ideal physical state.*

My body is now transforming to accommodate my every wish. I am radiant in my high-vibin' energy and able to light up any room. *Your turn*: I am _____. Why is it becoming so easy for me to feel this way now?

What are you loving and appreciating about yourself or your day or life right now and why?

_____

_____

_____

_____

_____

_____

_____

_____

_____

_____

Intentions for My Day (Or tomorrow)

What words describe my day? I am feeling _____. I am being _____. I am having _____. I am doing _____. How will I look and feel at the end of the day? Imagine it now.

It's time to take the next obvious step toward my goal. What actions can I take that I believe will help my body look and feel the way I want it to? If I had an unlimited amount of time, what would I love to do that gets my body moving, feels good to eat, makes me smile, or just feels therapeutic or good for me? I am feeling inspired to...

Move My Body by...	Spoil Myself with...	Do More Self Care like...
_____	_____	_____
_____	_____	_____
_____	_____	_____
_____	_____	_____
_____	_____	_____
_____	_____	_____
_____	_____	_____
_____	_____	_____
_____	_____	_____
_____	_____	_____
_____	_____	_____

I am circling my favorite activities and taking the time to nurture or spoil myself more by doing one of them every day or week or so on this day and time:

_____

I am feeling more inspired every day to take the next step toward my goal. *Your turn*: I am_____.

Which activity is the most fun or satisfying to think about?
And which one(s) do you plan to do first and why?

_____
_____
_____
_____
_____
_____
_____
_____
_____
_____

Intentions for My Day (Or tomorrow)

What words describe my day? I am feeling _____. I am being _____. I am having _____. I am doing _____. How will I look and feel at the end of the day? Imagine it now.

It's time to practice my belief and expectation of things working out for me. I am becoming as aligned with my ideal body as I believe I am. While I love knowing that I'm not done becoming who I am, I also love accepting myself exactly as I am. It feels so good and allows more good things to happen for me!

When it comes to positive changes in my body, I expect it to...

_____

_____

When it comes to how my body feels, I have faith that...

_____

When it comes to my energy level, I expect it to be better every day as I...

_____

When it comes to eating, I appreciate and enjoy any food I choose to eat without guilt or fear because I know my body feels good about it if I feel good about it. If I can fully enjoy eating it, my vibrational energy stays high and that's very good for me. The foods that may be considered indulgent or unhealthy that I intend to fully enjoy are...

_____

I also enjoy eating...

_____

For the sake of my body, just because I know it will feel good, I am feeling inspired to try...

_____

I am really good at getting a restful night's sleep because...

_____

What if I were to go to sleep each night expecting to wake up with *abundant* energy? And what if I were to wake up every day expecting to have that energy stay with me *all* day? How much better would my day go with that expectation?

_____

What if I practiced that thought long enough for it to be my belief? The more I practice the more often it happens that way. Isn't it great to know that my beliefs and positive emotions are making things happen for me?

Going forward, I expect to have even more confidence in my body because...

_____

I believe my body is functioning perfectly in every way and continually bringing itself into balance as I find myself more at ease. I am naturally vibrant and strong and my body is capable of...

_____

_____

I expect to be better every day at feeling how I want to feel because I am determined and...

_____

_____

Things are always working out for me and when it comes to my body, I choose to trust that things are working out for me because...

_____

My favorite part of this working out for me is...

_____

I expect things to continue going well for me because...

_____

Let's say I'm feeling exactly how I want to feel, or better, and I'm having the kind of day I would love to have every day. What would I be doing right now? Where would I be? What would I be thinking about? Who would I be with? What are we talking about or planning to do?

_____

_____

_____

I am thankful for my perfectly functioning body working with me to feel better every day in every way. I love being in this body and I appreciate you because...

_____

_____

_____

I want to trust that all is well with me and always will be. I feel limitless in my ability to...

_____

I am open and receptive to all the gifts that are available to me. With every breath I take, I am breathing in more energy and vitality. _Your turn_: I am _____.

What part of your desired outcome do you believe in most and why?

_____

_____

_____

Intentions for My Day (Or tomorrow)

What words describe my day? I am feeling _____. I am being _____. I am having _____. I am doing _____. How will I look and feel at the end of the day? Imagine it now.

Since I am focusing on solutions, what are some additional ways that I can balance and strengthen my energy?

What if I became more aware of the strengthening energy that's all around me? What forms of energy have I been noticing? I like knowing that I can find it wherever I go if I'm looking for it. Do I notice that I feel differently when I'm around nature, water, trees, the sun or moon, or any other conditions? What are they and how does it make me feel?

_____

_____

_____

_____

_____

_____

_____

What else can I do to cultivate my energy? There are so many ways to tap into my natural-born energy. Moving my body gets my circulation and life force energy flowing and that will naturally increase my energy, as well as the deeper breathing that comes along with it.

Here are some suggestions, but check with your physician before trying them if you have any back issues or health conditions of any kind.

- ★ Consider setting a timer daily for 10 minutes before breakfast, lunch, or dinner, then put on some fun music and dance like you've never danced before.
- ★ Rebounding - try one of the ways astronauts have been known to bounce back after an excursion: rebounding on a mini trampoline. Some of the well-known benefits are stimulating lymph, rebuilding lost bone or tissue, strengthening your core, and improving balance and muscle tone.
- ★ Tap into the energy around you by connecting to the three life forces that are continuously providing us with energy: the earth, the universe, and nature. Intentionally tuning in to this unlimited supply of energy, as needed or on a daily basis, can help you feel more balanced, energized, and uplifted.
  - o This can be done anywhere, anytime, and preferably standing. Outside in bare feet is even better.
  - o Place your hands with your palms face down toward the earth.
  - o With your attention on your palms, breathe in with the intent of drawing in the earth's magnetic energy. Feel the energy come up to meet you.
  - o Imagine your feet connected to the earth's core. Try seeing it as a golden crystal. Allow your whole body to breathe it in. Allow it to soothe and strengthen you.
  - o Try it again with your eyes closed; breathe in to the count of 2 or 3 and out for 4 or 5 with your attention on the palms.
  - o Then face your palms upward and take a moment to connect with the universe's revitalizing energy. Breathe in with the intent of taking in the pure positive life-force energy that's all around you and always flowing to you and through you. Allow it to breathe new life into you.
  - o Try it again with your eyes closed and breathe in to the count of 2 or 3 and out for 4 or 5 with your attention on the palms.
  - o Lastly, hold your hands up in front of your chest and face the palms outward and intend to breathe in the energy of nature or all plant life. Visualize your favorite trees all around you.
  - o If desired, bring your palms together in front of your chest and set an intention, such as "I am now refreshed and energized, guarded and guided in this golden light."
  - o This is also a great time to send out wishes for wellbeing to loved ones or everyone if you'd like to.

Feeling your way into anything you wish to experience in life is all about the quality of your intention. And once you see the results even once, your belief and expectation becomes stronger. You're inevitably becoming how you want to be in every way.

- ★ Qi Gong (pronounced "chi-gung") is one of the best ways known to cultivate energy. It's like a moving meditation that involves coordinating your breath with flowing movements. It can easily increase blood flow, clear stagnant energy, and promote balance and healing of the body. Practicing it daily keeps the doctor away, I say. The more you practice, the more connected you become to your body, your breath, and your core energy. I suggest "Qi Gong for Self Healing" or "Qi Gong for More Energy" by my Qi Gong training instructor, Lee Holden.
- ★ EFT (Emotional Freedom Technique) also known as Meridian Tapping - tapping on acupressure points as you say affirmations. It has helped people around the world relieve stress, pain or illness, as well as increase energy and abundance, and more. If desired, I offer 1:1 EFT coaching online, but with a more positive focus.
- ★ Acupressure points for increasing energy. There are pressure points for just about anything.
- ★ And of course there is meditation, guided meditation, yoga, hand mudras, and the list goes on and on. Once you try something new, you discover even more healing modalities and wonder why you never heard of them before. They show up when you're ready, and if it's in your best interest, it will feel good.

Feel free to research any of the above and only do what feels comfortable for you. You just need to pick something that you'll enjoy, and you won't be able to get enough of it. It feels so good when you notice a clearer mind and more boundless energy from a new practice, and you will find yourself missing it when you skip it for a day or two.

Last but not least, ask yourself daily: "How does it feel when I allow myself to have twice as much energy right now?" I am going to have energy all day, every day. *Your turn*: I am _____.

What has always been your favorite part about being who you are and why?

_____

_____

_____

_____

_____

_____

_____

_____

_____

_____

Intentions for My Day (Or tomorrow)

What words describe my day? I am feeling _____. I am being _____. I am having _____. I am doing _____. How will I look and feel at the end of the day? Imagine it now. Here's your new mantra: I look and feel younger every day!

I am practicing how it feels to be in the qualities and energy of whatever my desire is for my physical body. There's no limit to what I can do or what I can become if I can feel that my desire is a part of me and who I am. Going forward, I am doing my best to practice being one with this energy. I am living and breathing it. What are the qualities or characteristics that I'm in or intend to be in? I can write down what first comes to mind, and then list words from A-Z that describe the way I look and feel and act when I am at this higher level of confidence. I am a magnet for all my life's wishes. I am...

_____   _____   _____
_____   _____   _____
_____   _____   _____
_____   _____   _____
_____   _____   _____
_____   _____   _____
_____   _____   _____
_____   _____   _____
_____   _____   _____
_____   _____   _____
_____   _____   _____

What's it like to have a clear mind, a comfortable body, and allow myself to be in the joy of who I am all the time, if not already? How does it feel to close my eyes right now and imagine what it's like to be there and be living it? How did it feel?

_____

_____

If desired, 1) Make note of anything you practiced in the past ten days that felt good to you and you wish to continue. 2) Add your favorite thought-provoking question and affirmation to the list you started.

I am better every day at feeling how I wish to feel. I am full of ease and energy. *Your turn*: I am
_____. How much more am I able to feel this way in the days ahead?

It's a couple months or so from now and people are complimenting you on some positive changes they see, or perhaps they sense this by how you're acting. What are they noticing?

_____

_____

_____

Intentions for My Day (Or tomorrow)

What words describe my day? I am feeling _____. I am being _____. I am having _____. I am doing _____. How will I look and feel at the end of the day? Imagine it now.

More Appreciation & Intentions

What was my favorite part about today or this past week?

_____

What are three or more things I felt appreciation for and why?

_____
_____
_____
_____

I appreciate my body for...

_____
_____

What are some things that happened or that I did that made me feel more energetic or my body feel more comfortable?

_____
_____
_____

I appreciate myself for how much I am intending to breathe in more energy, clarity, and harmony and also for choosing to practice thinking and feeling how I truly wish to feel in the following ways:
At home, I am...

_____
_____
_____

At work, I am...

_____
_____
_____

With my friends, I am...

_____
_____
_____

In my personal time, I am...

_____
_____

I am feeling *really* fortunate when I think of...

_____

_____

_____

If anything stressful happened, how do I want things to go if it were to happen again? Play it out in your mind and see it turn out the way you would like it to. What if you added some comedy? How would you describe it?

_____

_____

_____

Did that make you feel better? Perhaps you could draw your scene and recall it if it happens again. If you can find a way to be amused about something that causes stress, it can't harm you or take you out of a good-feeling place.

Who or what am I feeling especially thankful for and why?

_____

If desired, send out wishes for more joy and wellbeing to them or anyone you will see in the next 24 hours.

Intentions for the Days Ahead

What's my intention for this coming week or so? How do I expect things to go? What are all the words or phrases that describe it and how do I feel at the end of the week? And if there's anything I wish to accomplish, what is it and how does it feel to have it done?

_____

_____

_____

_____

_____

_____

_____

_____

_____

_____

_____

Now, close your eyes and take about thirty seconds to visualize your week the way you want it to be. It will happen as I expect it to, or better.

★ *First thing in the morning, ask:* "How do I wish to feel throughout my day today? I choose to feel _____."

Fill this page with words of appreciation for all the wellbeing and abundance that's on its way to you.

Harmony

Peace

Clarity

Thank You

Inner Strength

Mindfulness

Bliss

For the next ten days, the topic will mainly be on what you wrote on Day 1 as your desired end result for...

I am Feeling: _____. Please fill it in once again.

My happiness is based on how I feel and how I view myself and my life. It basically sets the tone for the quality of my life experience. Happiness is always a choice I can make and I deserve to feel good! There's no limit to the amount of happiness I can achieve. *Tell your desire what you want, why you want it, what it will do for you when you have it, and how it will change your life. Fill the page with as many details as possible.*

Dear Happiness,

_____
_____
_____
_____
_____
_____
_____
_____
_____
_____
_____
_____
_____
_____
_____
_____
_____
_____
_____
_____
_____
_____

I keep finding more ways to allow myself to feel even better. I find reasons to smile every day. I'm ready to feel as good as I can feel from morning to night. And in order to do this well, I choose to love and accept myself. I am now matching the vibration of the reality I wish to achieve. *Your turn*: I am _____.

Intentions for My Day (Or tomorrow)

What words describe my day? I am feeling _____. I am being _____. I am having _____. I am doing _____. How will I look and feel at the end of the day? Imagine it now.

What does feeling happy mean to me?

_____

_____

_____

Take yourself to a place and time that felt beyond wonderful to you, or somewhere you'd like to be. When I am feeling the happiest I've ever felt...

I am spending my time thinking about...

_____

_____

Emotionally, I am feeling...

_____

_____

Physically, I am feeling...

_____

_____

I am feeling more confident about...

_____

_____

I am being...

_____

_____

I am having more fun doing...

_____

_____

I am doing more of what I wish to do. I am...

_____

_____

My life feels better because I am...

_____

_____

_____

I am able to achieve unconditional happiness, where nothing needs to happen in order for me to feel happy. I'm just happy. I am now aligning with the energy of blissful wellbeing. *Your turn*: I am
_____.

What do you love most about how you're feeling now and why?

_____

_____

_____

_____

_____

_____

_____

_____

_____

_____

_____

_____

_____

_____

_____

_____

_____

_____

_____

_____

_____

_____

_____

_____

_____

Intentions for My Day (Or tomorrow)

What words describe my day? I am feeling _____. I am being _____. I am having _____. I am doing _____. How will I look and feel at the end of the day? Imagine it now.

I am doing my best to completely accept myself as I am. I'm truly better every day in every way and in every area of my life. I am now allowing myself to feel as happy and free as I was born to be. This is my powerful intention, and so it must be. I am creating an atmosphere for success and there's no limit to the amount of happiness I can have. It's a feeling that keeps building and there's no going back. Is there anything that I believe is in the way of living a happier life?

_____

_____

What is one thing I could say or do to change that belief? Is it something I can change or look at in a different way? A way that helps me feel better about it?

_____

_____

How can I support myself in the ways that I believe will help me feel happier more of the time? Is there anything that comes to mind?

_____

What am I already doing that I want to continue doing because it makes me happy?

_____

_____

What people, places, activities, special moments, or other things make me happy? What really excites me or brings an automatic smile to my face?

_____

_____

_____

Is there anything else I can think of that I may want to change or stop or start doing that will make me feel more aligned with my true desires, or the person I'm becoming? What would give me a feeling of relief or total elation?

_____

_____

_____

How does it feel to honor myself? What does that mean to me?

_____

_____

Think of three or more things I can do to honor myself more. Are there any opinions, wishes, or other ideas that I'd like to start listening to, that I may have stifled or ignored in the past?

_____

_____

_____

How much better is my life when I completely accept myself and respect my own opinions and wishes? How does it feel to stop judging myself and appreciate my uniqueness? What am I ready to accept and appreciate about myself?

_____

_____

How free do I feel when I do everything that feels good to me and let go of anything that doesn't? What if I started small and tried doing some things differently if I knew it would make me feel happier? What comes to mind?

_____

_____

How does it feel when I allow myself to give as much to myself as I've given to others, or more? In what ways do I do that now?

_____

_____

I feel happiest when I am...

_____

What are some new thoughts I could practice to align with more joy?

_____

_____

If my happiness could tell me what it will do for me and what it wants me to do to have more of it, what would it say?

_____

_____

My success and satisfaction with my life can be considered equal to the quality of my thoughts. The more I love and accept myself, the higher my level of joy and success can be. In the days ahead, I am allowing myself to feel happy where I am and excited for what's to come. _Your turn_: I am _____.

*** . . . . * . . . . ✦ . . * ✦ * . . . * * . . . ✦ . . . . ✦ * . . . * * . . . ✦ . . . . * ✦ . . . * * . . . ✦ . . . . * *

What do you love about the idea of living a life where every area of your life feels deeply satisfying, and why?

_____

_____

_____

_____

Intentions for My Day (Or tomorrow)

What words describe my day? I am feeling _____. I am being _____. I am having _____. I am doing _____. How will I look and feel at the end of the day? Imagine it now.

Day 34 _____

I love how much I value myself now, and more so every day. It's helping me feel important enough to put myself first. I deserve to treat myself well. It was easy to start feeling more appreciation for being who I am when I realized that I wouldn't want to be anyone else. It's becoming natural for me to practice being the constant friend I've always wanted.

What does it feel like to be my own best friend? What does that mean to me and what are the words that would describe it?

_____
_____
_____

How does it feel to give myself the love and support I've always deserved? Do I notice when I'm saying yes to things I'd rather say no to? Or when I'm ignoring my own needs or wishes? In what ways am I there for myself like I've been there for others?

_____
_____
_____

How does my life change when I begin to listen to my internal voice? The one that's constantly guiding me on a path to more joy by way of instinctive thoughts or emotions? I love when I allow myself to do what makes me happy because...

_____
_____
_____

How worthy of my desires do I allow myself to feel? What is *finally* making me aware of all the unique talents and gifts I have to offer just by being me? When I feel unconditional love and appreciation for myself, what is that like? Write or think of numerous words or phrases that show appreciation for my qualities, including my mind, body, personality, skills, and anything else I can think of. My greatest gifts are...

_____   _____
_____   _____
_____   _____
_____   _____
_____   _____

How good does it feel when I decide that my words are the only ones that matter for my own wellbeing and happiness? If I ever felt like I was unwanted, unimportant, or not enough in any way, what would I tell myself that would validate the reasons it was completely untrue then and now?

_____
_____
_____

What if I could start being that voice in my head now? The one that says what I need or want to hear *all* the time? Like the kind of words that instill a belief in my true value? What is one sentence that defines my true value?

_____

How does it feel to be the happiest and truest version of me that's right here beneath my layers? How would I describe my personality when I've stripped away any guardedness I may have had? When I arrive wherever I go without any pretense whatsoever and I am completely myself and only myself, I am acting and feeling...

_____

_____

_____

_____

_____

From now on I allow myself to be the one that whispers in my ear and offers all the encouragement I could ever want. The more I practice this self-talk, the more it gets instilled and remains in the forefront of my mind. All self-doubt has left me, and I feel free. I am worthy of all good things. I am believing this now more than ever. *Your turn*: I am _____.

You are meant to feel wonderful and believe great things about yourself. *What are the words you may have wanted to hear as a child that will stay with you now and allow you to flourish?*

_____

_____

_____

_____

_____

_____

_____

_____

_____

_____

_____

_____

Intentions for My Day (Or tomorrow)

What words describe my day? I am feeling _____. I am being _____. I am having _____. I am doing _____. How will I look and feel at the end of the day? Imagine it now.

What if all I needed to do was feel really good about myself and what's happening around me to start attracting more of what I want into my life? Since I can feel my way into any reality I wish to achieve and I can talk myself into anything, how do I want to feel? Each day I guide myself to find the feeling place I wish to have.

All I need to do is ask: How do I want to feel? What words will describe the feeling of having it? When I want to redirect any negative thoughts or emotions so that I can feel better, all I need to do is ask: What is my favorite thing about this day, this person, or this situation? What is the solution? What would love do? How does my inner being feel about it? Or what else can I do to get my mind off of this?

And then I remind myself that I am the master of my mind. I am the master of my day. And the master of my life. And I'm going to practice the state of mind that I wish to be in to align with whatever desire I'm wanting to be a vibrational match to in that moment.

So, how do I want to feel right now? What words will describe the feeling of having it? What is my focused attention on recently? What is my favorite thing about this day, this time in my life, or the people in my life? If there's anything I'm working through, what is the solution? What would love do? How does my inner being feel about it? How much better am I able to feel today? Now is the time to convince myself. *Respond to each of these questions below and be your most convincing enthusiastic self, or just freely write what feels right to you.*

_____
_____
_____
_____
_____
_____
_____
_____
_____
_____
_____
_____
_____
_____
_____
_____
_____
_____
_____
_____
_____
_____

I am becoming one with the energy of pure joy and making it mine. How much more joy can I let myself feel right now? *If desired, look at any words written above that hold a positive emotion and imagine you're breathing it in.*

How much more am I able to feel the harmony in my body and breath? *Close your eyes, slow your breath, and ask again. Give your body time to respond.*

This is what I do when I want to feel better. I choose to guide my thoughts like this until it feels natural for me. Until it's second nature and I begin to see all the wonderful things that I'm attracting with my positive thoughts and energy. Every precious moment of my life is worth taking the time to do this. It just feels so good.

I am feeling as in charge of how I feel as I let myself be. And I am as happy as I let myself be. I am in charge. I decide. I make the rules. I get to choose. If I'm wanting things to feel better in my life, I'm going to create more fun wherever I go. *Your turn:* I am _____.
Why is it becoming so easy for me to feel good any time I want?

What else are you loving and appreciating about yourself or your life right now and why?

_____
_____
_____
_____
_____
_____
_____
_____
_____
_____
_____
_____
_____
_____
_____
_____
_____
_____
_____
_____

Intentions for My Day (Or tomorrow)

What words describe my day? I am feeling _____. I am being _____. I am having _____. I am doing _____. How much more am I able to smile throughout my day? Inner guidance, show me how it feels in the days and weeks ahead. I am open and receptive to feeling better every day in every way and in every area of my life.

It's time to take the next obvious step toward my goal. The vibration of wellbeing has a higher frequency and I must be aligning with it because I'm feeling *so* good. That's a telltale sign. So this day is all about thinking of ways that I can feel *so* much joy that my body's energy continues to vibrate at this higher frequency more of the time. The more consistent I am about feeling good, the more I retain this higher energy, and the longer it stays with me.

How can I intentionally raise my vibration anytime I want? What is one thing that first comes to mind? What makes me feel high on life?

_____

Since thoughts have their own vibrational energy, the more positive my thoughts, the higher my frequency is. What are some of my favorite affirmations that always seem to lift me up?

_____
_____
_____

I can also focus daily on my *favorite* things and appreciate what I have in my life. What comes to mind?

_____
_____
_____

I can keep my favorite high-vibin' song running in my head. No, I'm *not* kidding! What is it?

_____

I can practice regular meditation or deep breathing, which allows me to release resistance, gain clarity, and instantly raise my vibration. If not meditation/breathing, what do I enjoy that is equivalent to this?

_____
_____

I'm also in a higher vibration when I'm feeling at *ease*, or any feeling that feels good to me. What am I doing that brings me to that state of mind?

_____
_____

I can smile and laugh more. What am I doing now or what else could I do that makes me smile and laugh more?

_____
_____

I can focus on my heart energy and a feeling of love and appreciation for anything I wish, including myself. Try it now. What are some loving moments that make me happy when I think of them?

_____
_____

I can spend time doing things that I'm passionate about. What are my passion projects?

_____

_____

I can spend time in nature, listen to music, watch comedies, sing, hum, dance, or do anything that's fun for me.

Write a list of habits or activities that you want to try or do more of that you believe will make you really happy and raise your vibration, and include how you act and feel when you're doing them.

This is what I'm doing	This is how I'm acting and feeling
_____	_____
_____	_____
_____	_____
_____	_____
_____	_____
_____	_____
_____	_____
_____	_____
_____	_____
_____	_____

I *love* knowing that the higher my vibration, the higher level of wellbeing I have and the higher the level of abundance will be in my life. I believe in my own wellbeing now, and no matter how good I was feeling before, I intend to feel even better.

I am feeling more inspired every day to take the next step toward my goal. *Your turn*: I am

_____.

Which activity is the most fun or satisfying to think about?
And which one(s) do you plan to do first and why?

_____

_____

_____

_____

_____

_____

_____

Intentions for My Day (Or tomorrow)

What words describe my day? I am feeling _____. I am being _____. I am having _____. I am doing _____. How will I look and feel at the end of the day? Imagine it now.

It's time to practice my belief and expectation to feel more happiness in my life, where I'm feeling like a magnet that attracts all good things to me. Where my attention goes, energy flows, and that's why I can create any reality I choose. What is my focused attention on? If not now, imagine I completely accept myself and have faith and trust that I am just right where I am. This is a life I love more every day. *Let your responses be from that standpoint.*

How much more happiness am I expecting in my life? What are the great things I'm expecting to work out for me?

_____

_____

I am happy to be...

_____

I am happy to have...

_____

I expect things to continue feeling better every day in every way because...

_____

How much has my level of expectation improved for how people should treat me and what are some examples of how they are treating me?

_____

_____

How does it feel to have a natural ability to confidently speak my mind? What is an example of something I've been speaking up about?

_____

_____

How much faith do I have in myself for letting others know what my needs are? What am I telling them I need or want, and how good am I at expecting them to respect my wishes?

_____

_____

What's it like to make decisions without feeling the need for anyone's approval? What are some decisions I'm making with total confidence?

_____

_____

How comfortable do I feel showing others my authentic self? In what ways am I doing this?

_____

_____

How am I good at supporting my own needs in the following areas:

With my family:

_____

With my partner:

_____

While at work:

_____

With friends:

_____

If I had a magic wand, what changes would I make that I believe would bring more joy into my life?

_____

_____

How would this make me feel and how would it change my life?

_____

_____

I believe it's achievable because...

_____

_____

My desired outcomes are finding their way to me. With every breath I take, I am breathing in more joy. Every cell in my body is *feeling* it with me. *Breathe in for two seconds, out for four or six. Try that once or twice, and then relax and breathe naturally.* Life is good for me and I feel free. I am believing in myself more every day. *Your turn*: I am _____.

How much more are you able to believe in your ability to achieve more self-confidence, happiness, or anything else you wish for yourself?
And what part of your desired outcome do you believe in most and why?

_____

_____

_____

Intentions for My Day (Or tomorrow)

What words describe my day? I am feeling _____. I am being _____. I am having _____. I am doing _____. How will I look and feel at the end of the day? Imagine it now. I am in the right place at the right time and always moving forward toward an even better place. I am better every day at trusting in this.

This is my day for positive solutions. The goal is to stay in a good-feeling place no matter what is happening. Sometimes the solution is just about looking at things differently, thinking of how I prefer to feel, or focusing on something else. So what are my positive solutions?

What are some things I can briefly think of that frequently or occasionally frustrate me and tend to take me out of a good-feeling place? Now write all the reasons each of these things won't matter in five minutes, an hour, a week, month, or year or more from now.

_____
_____
_____
_____
_____

Write down the ways that I can look at these issues differently or the complete opposite thought of what I was thinking about it before.

_____
_____
_____
_____

Write down the reasons that I'm not going to let it bother me next time, and why feeling good is more important to me.

_____
_____
_____

Another solution or way that I can use to relieve frustration is by...

_____
_____

If I ever feel down, I...

_____
_____

If I ever need to get myself out of a "stuck" feeling, I...

_____
_____

When I want to feel more focused or be more decisive, I...

_____
_____

What else have I been doing for myself that has helped me let go of any struggles I may have had? Are there any breakthroughs or milestones to acknowledge and commend myself for, no matter how big or small? What am I giving myself "permission" for that I may not have allowed myself to do in the past?

_____

_____

_____

_____

Do I have any self-doubting thoughts or limiting beliefs that may hinder my happiness? When I ask myself if they were my beliefs in the first place or if they're true, it can help me let them go. It's only true if I believe it. If desired, write them down, ask those questions, and then write the complete opposite of what they are, beginning with "I am." Practice replacing the old thought with the new affirmation if it comes up again.

_____

_____

_____

_____

_____

Going forward, to have more fun and feel more joy in my life, I am ready to…

_____

_____

_____

I am practicing thoughts that make me feel…

_____

I love how in charge I feel and how much better I feel at the end of the day. I am now attracting the circumstances that allow my happier, healthier life to unfold. And perfectly so. I am more at ease every day, no matter what is happening around me. *Your turn*: I am _____.

How much more optimistic are you able to feel about your life in general?
What are you feeling optimistic about now and why?

_____

_____

_____

_____

Intentions for My Day (Or tomorrow)

What words describe my day? I am feeling _____. I am being _____. I am having _____. I am doing _____. How will I look and feel at the end of the day? Imagine it now.

How I see myself is who I become. I intend to be in the qualities and energy of my most confident, loving, self-respecting, joyful, radiant self from now on. When this is a part of who I am, I am magnetic to all my desires and life just keeps getting better and better. What are the qualities I intend to be in and intend to stay in to the best of my ability? And what are the inspired actions I intend to take as a result of feeling this good? Write a list of each in the columns and use A-Z if desired.

_____   _____
_____   _____
_____   _____
_____   _____
_____   _____
_____   _____
_____   _____
_____   _____
_____   _____
_____   _____
_____   _____

How much more am I able to feel this way in the days ahead? Why is it suddenly so easy for me to have more joy-filled days?

If desired, 1) Make note of anything you practiced in the past ten days that felt good to you and you wish to continue. 2) Add your favorite thought-provoking question and affirmation to the list you started.

If I'm wanting to feel happier and have more fun, I am creating it wherever I go. I am as happy as I let myself be. And I am choosing to be at ease and full of joy! I am now achieving a level of happiness that is supporting my desire for total wellbeing. *Your turn*: I am _____.

If not already, imagine you're feeling happier than ever and you're wishing the same feeling for someone you know. *What would you tell them about how it feels and how easy it could be for them to feel this way too?*

_____
_____
_____
_____

Intentions for My Day (Or tomorrow)

What words describe my day? I am feeling _____. I am being _____. I am having _____. I am doing _____. How will I look and feel at the end of the day? Imagine it now.

More Appreciation & Intentions

A great way to attract and invite more happiness into my life is to feel appreciation for where I am and for what I have right now. When I have a sincere appreciation for what I've chosen for myself, whether it's a job, a partner, or something else, I'm putting the kind of positive energy into it that paves the way for a better future. So even if I'm not feeling quite fulfilled with something, I focus on the parts I like. And this way, I attract a better relationship, a better job, and better circumstances for all areas of my life, if desired.

What was my favorite part about today or this past week?

_____

_____

What are some things that happened or that I did that made me feel happy?

_____

_____

_____

I appreciate myself for how much I am choosing to love and appreciate where I am right now and find more ways to smile on a daily basis. At home, I am feeling happier when I...

_____

_____

While I'm at work, I am making a point to feel more appreciation for...

_____

_____

With my friends, I am appreciating...

_____

_____

With my partner or in my personal time, I love that...

_____

_____

If there is one favorite thing or one area of my life that makes me feel really happy to think about, what would that be? The more I think about it, the better I feel. And the better I feel, the more abundance will flow into my life. I'm opening myself up to *all* possibility. My favorite thing to think about that really lights me up is...

_____

What's it like and why do I love it so much? Details, please.

_____

_____

What are my favorite qualities about myself? I feel really good about myself recently because I am...

_____

_____

Every day I get better at...

_____

Intentions for the Days Ahead

One of the ways I can stay in a good-feeling place or feel more satisfied with my life, and prevent feeling "stuck" or unfulfilled, is to always have something of interest to look forward to. I can always have a feeling of satisfaction with my life when I'm moving toward something I am wanting, such as a passion project or an upcoming class or social event. What am I looking forward to this week and why?

_____

_____

_____

_____

What am I looking forward to this month?

_____

_____

_____

_____

What am I looking forward to this coming year?

_____

_____

_____

_____

_____

_____

_____

Is there anything new I'm planning to do/learn/buy that I'm excited about? What is it and why do I want this?

_____

_____

Now, close your eyes and take about thirty seconds to visualize how you want tomorrow and the coming week to go.

★ *First thing in the morning, ask:* "How do I wish to feel throughout my day today? I choose to feel _____."

For the next ten days, the topic will mainly be on what you wrote on Day 1 as your desired end result for...

My Home and Family are: _____. Please fill it in once again. These next ten days can be about your home or family life, or perhaps a family member who doesn't live with you. The focus is on improving the relationships in a way that supports your wellbeing. What's your home life like now, and what would you absolutely love for it to be like? Tell your home life or your family what you want, how it will help you and/or them, and how it will change each of your lives. Fill the page with as many details as possible.

Dear Home/Family,

_____

_____

_____

_____

_____

_____

_____

_____

_____

_____

_____

_____

_____

_____

_____

_____

_____

_____

_____

_____

_____

_____

I am making my intentions known and all that I wish for is making its way to me with effortless ease. *Your turn*:
I am_____. So many things are working out for me. Thank you!

Intentions for My Day (Or tomorrow)

What words describe my day? I am feeling _____. I am being _____. I am having _____. I am doing _____. How will I look and feel at the end of the day? Imagine it now.

What's it like when I've achieved my desired outcome for my home or family life, if any different than now? It's good to envision this for us while appreciating where we are now. How do I think we would be acting and feeling?

We are spending more time talking about...

_____

Our relationship, or my relationship with myself, has grown even stronger and more comfortable. It feels like...

_____

I am/we are feeling better in general about...

_____

I am feeling more connected to my home life or family because...

_____

I am/ We are being...

_____

I am having more fun because...

_____

I am doing more of what I wish to do at home. We are/I am...

_____

Life *feels* better because...

_____

_____

Just deciding to surrender and trust in things working out great for us, while keeping in mind that we're not done becoming what we can be together, is a wonderful way to invite more great things to happen for us. I am now aligning with the energy of an even happier home life. *Your turn*: I am _____

What part of your current home life do you love most and why?

_____

_____

_____

Intentions for My Day (Or tomorrow)

What words describe my day? I am feeling _____. I am being _____. I am having _____. I am doing _____. How will I look and feel at the end of the day? Imagine it now.

I am creating an atmosphere for success in achieving an even happier home life. Does it feel like anything needs to happen in order for me to align with it? If I change how I look at things, I can change the energy around the circumstances, and therefore things must change.

What is going well for me at home or with my family?

_____

_____

The habits or activities I enjoy at home are...

_____

_____

The habits or activities that are not feeling right at home are...

_____

_____

If I had a magic wand, what changes would I make at home?

_____

_____

_____

_____

_____

_____

_____

How do I think this would affect me or anyone at home with me? How would we benefit from these changes?

_____

_____

_____

_____

I believe it's achievable because...

_____

_____

Home life feels wonderful when...

_____

_____

I feel happiest when I am/we are spending time doing...

_____

What state of mind do I think I need to be in to achieve an even happier home life? And what are some new thoughts I could practice to align with it?

_____

_____

_____

_____

_____

_____

If my family or significant other could have things their way, what do I believe they would ask for, and what would that be like for me?

_____

_____

_____

_____

_____

_____

_____

_____

_____

Today and in the days ahead, I am creating an atmosphere for success in achieving a happier home life.
Your turn: I am _____.

What do you love about the direction your home/family life is headed toward and why?

_____

_____

_____

_____

_____

_____

_____

_____

Intentions for My Day (Or tomorrow)

What words describe my day? I am feeling _____. I am being _____. I am having _____. I am doing _____. How will I look and feel at the end of the day? Imagine it now.

Write all your family members' names below on the left side, leaving several lines between each one. Include children, parents, and siblings, or more, even if they don't live with you. As if they were sitting in front of you, tell each of them one at a time; 1) What you appreciate about them. 2) What your favorite qualities are about them. 3) What you would like the relationship to be like between you and why. 4) How you would like them to feel when they're with you and 5) How you would like to feel when you're with them. Don't skip any of these points for each person. Use extra paper if necessary.

_____

_____

_____

_____

_____

_____

_____

_____

_____

_____

_____

_____

_____

_____

_____

_____

_____

_____

_____

_____

_____

_____

_____

_____

_____

_____

_____

_____

_____

_____

_____

_____

If desired, and if it feels good to you, consider having these imaginary conversations each night before you go to bed or before you will be seeing them. Addressing a symbol of them can help. Even though they won't know you're doing this, your new perception shifts your energy and changes the circumstances around the relationship for the better. It's a great way to feel more connected to them, even for those who have distanced themselves from you. This process has the ability to heal any relationship, so don't be surprised if a relationship is dramatically improved in some way. You may even hear from someone you haven't spoken to in years. If nothing else, it has the potential to help you feel much better about anything that may have felt uncomfortable before.

If you have a desire for a new home or improving your home in some way, imagine it's right in front of you or use a symbol of it and tell it what you love about it. For example, "I love how cozy and comfortable and spacious you feel," and continue in much detail about each room and what you enjoy using that's in it or outside in the yard. Being in the energy of this house invites it to show up for you.

I am creating a more satisfying relationship with each of my family members. *Your turn*: I am

_____.

How are you feeling today and why do you think that is?
If you think you could feel even better, what are the words that would describe it?
Breathe in the meaning of each word as it's written.

_____

_____

_____

_____

_____

_____

_____

_____

_____

_____

_____

_____

_____

_____

_____

Intentions for My Day (Or tomorrow)

What words describe my day? I am feeling _____. I am being _____. I am having _____. I am doing _____. How will I look and feel at the end of the day? Imagine it now.

How do I want to feel when I'm at home or with my family? This week is all about practicing the feeling of having my home life feel even better for me. There's no limit to the amount of happiness my family or partner and I can have.

Having things run more smoothly and be more fun or pleasant for everyone will benefit us by...

_____

_____

_____

I am ready to let this happen because...

_____

_____

_____

Having it is changing our/my life by...

_____

_____

_____

It makes things easier by...

_____

_____

I love how good it feels when it's all happening because...

_____

_____

_____

What is it like for me or for us when we're there? Think of everything being as easy and comfortable and fun as I'd like it to be. What would an ideal day be like for us, from morning to night? What are the words or phrases that describe it and how does it feel?

_____

_____

_____

_____

_____

_____

_____

_____

_____

_____

_____

_____

_____

_____

_____

_____

How does it feel to walk into my home when everything is just the way I want it to be?

_____

Now close your eyes and imagine what it's like. Think of all the little details like the routine, the conversations, and how it looks and feels. I am keeping the image impressed upon my mind. I am becoming one with the energy of my desire and making it mine. I am now achieving an even happier home life. _Your turn_: I am _____. Why does this feel like it's getting easier for me every day?

What are you loving and appreciating about your day or life right now and why?

_____

_____

_____

_____

_____

_____

_____

_____

_____

_____

_____

_____

_____

_____

Intentions for My Day (Or tomorrow)

What words describe my day? I am feeling _____. I am being _____. I am having _____. I am doing _____. How will I look and feel at the end of the day? Imagine it now.

It's time to take the next obvious step toward my goal. What actions can I take that I believe will help me achieve what I want for my home or family? *Write a list of habits or activities you would enjoy doing at home or wish to do with your family that you believe will bring you closer together and/or support your wellbeing. Perhaps these are things you've thought of before or are coming to mind now. The sky's the limit. What are you doing? Where are you going? What are you talking about? What are you planning? What are you learning? What are you making? What's for dinner? What are you sharing with each other?*

_____   _____   _____

_____   _____   _____

_____   _____   _____

_____   _____   _____

_____   _____   _____

_____   _____   _____

_____   _____   _____

_____   _____   _____

_____   _____   _____

_____   _____   _____

_____   _____   _____

_____   _____   _____

_____   _____   _____

Circle your favorites and consider picking one of them to do each week or so or per month. I am feeling more inspired every day to take that next step. *Your turn*: I am_____.

Which activity feels the most fun or satisfying to think about?
And which do you intend to do first and why?

_____

_____

_____

_____

_____

_____

_____

Intentions for My Day (Or tomorrow)

What words describe my day? I am feeling _____. I am being _____. I am having _____. I am doing _____. How will I look and feel at the end of the day? Imagine it now.

It's time to practice my belief and expectation of things working out for me and my family. Some of the best times we've had together are...

_____
_____
_____
_____

I believe there are more good times coming. Here's what I see for us...

_____
_____
_____
_____
_____
_____

Here's what I wish for us in the coming year or so...

_____
_____
_____
_____
_____
_____
_____
_____

When it comes to how much fun I expect us to keep having together, I think of...

_____
_____
_____
_____

I think my family and I are on solid ground when it comes to...

_____
_____
_____

I believe my family relationships can get even stronger than they are now because...

_____
_____
_____

What's it like to have an unwavering trust in things working out for us in the best possible way, even better than I imagined? Imagine concerns fading away and a tremendous sense of freedom and relief taking over. How does that feel? What is working out for us? Describe how easy things have become.

_____

_____

_____

_____

I expect things to continue going well for us because...

_____

_____

If it was happening right now and I felt how I wanted to feel and we were having the kind of day I would love to have every day with my family, what would we be planning together for this weekend? Include all of what we're doing, what everyone will love about it, and how it feels when we're enjoying the experience together.

_____

_____

_____

_____

_____

_____

_____

_____

I believe in my ability to achieve anything I wish for. I love where we are, but also love knowing an even greater home life is available to me and I am now aligning with it. I am open and receptive to all the gifts that are available to us and letting go of how it will happen.

I trust that all is well with us and always will be. Could this be what it feels like to be in a great place? My family and I are always in the right place at the right time and moving toward an even better place, individually and with each other. *Your turn*: I am_____.

What is your favorite wish for your home or family that you believe in most and why?

_____

_____

_____

_____

Intentions for My Day (Or tomorrow)

What words describe my day? I am feeling _____. I am being _____. I am having _____. I am doing _____. How will I look and feel at the end of the day? Imagine it now.

When it comes to family, it can get a little more complicated when trying to stay in a good-feeling place. We care so much about our loved ones and we want what's best for them. We want them to be safe and make choices that are good for them. And sometimes we just wish we didn't worry about them. And this goes for the children *and* the adults. But if there's a desire to make things better somehow, there's always a way.

Is there anything going on currently at home or with family that I wish to find a positive solution for? If desired, think of a recent situation.

I can focus on a solution by deciding how I want things to be. What's the best possible outcome that could happen? What would I rather have happen if I could replay the scene or have it turn out that way the next time it occurs, if applicable?

_____
_____
_____
_____
_____
_____
_____

Are there options or anything I can do that will make things easier before it happens or during if any issues come up again? What are some other options that come to mind or steps that I can take to improve the circumstances?

_____
_____
_____
_____
_____
_____

How would it feel to have this situation be really comfortable for me? What are the words to describe the total relief and joy I feel when a better outcome has taken place? *Take a moment to close your eyes and think of it.*

_____
_____
_____

If this or another situation between family members isn't directly involving me but I tend to get in the middle of it, what's the best possible outcome without my involvement? Can I see myself letting it go and putting my attention on what I prefer to be doing with my time?

Can I decide right now to start expecting good things to happen for them? What are the words of trust in having everything work out for the best or as it's meant to?

_____
_____

In what way would I like to see things turn out on their own? What's the best possible outcome that could happen without my involvement?

_____

_____

_____

_____

_____

_____

What are the words of relief I feel when things turn out better than expected without any further effort on my part?

_____

_____

_____

The moment I decide to let things be, I am often delighted by how quickly things can improve on their own. And I *love* the idea of saving myself unnecessary stress.

I can close my eyes right now and see my desired end result for each situation. I see everyone involved doing better and feel that it's all that I hoped it would be, or better. We're on the same wavelength and enjoying ourselves and it all feels so easy. That being said, if it doesn't feel good to think about this particular situation, I think of another area of my life that *does* feel good. Putting my attention on any area of my life that I feel really good about is allowing all areas of my life to become better and easier.

What else can I do to improve my family relationships? If I want to improve them, I need to feel confident in myself and happy about the relationship. Am I acting confident and expressing myself clearly and calmly in each relationship? When I change how I'm acting, they will too.

Let go of any doubt that things are now improving, as you focus on how you want things to be.

As my wellbeing and desire to feel good becomes the most important thing to me, I get better at letting things like this go. I can transform any stressful or troubling situation into a peaceful one. My family life is becoming all I want it to be. My energy is contagious! *Your turn*: I am _____.

What do you love about being even closer to your family members in an easy, relaxed manner and why?

_____

_____

_____

_____

Intentions for My Day (Or tomorrow)

What words describe my day? I am feeling _____. I am being _____. I am having _____. I am doing _____. How will I look and feel at the end of the day? Imagine it now.

Day 49 _____

I am practicing how it feels to be in the qualities and energy of my happiest home life. Fill this page with words or phrases that describe what our home life and our newly improved relationship is like. No matter how good it is, it can be even better. Wouldn't it be wonderful if my living by example would cause a lovely ripple effect? I'm growing and changing and all circumstances must change with me. What are the qualities or energy we're in and how do I see my home or family changing? What are the words that describe how we're acting or feeling when we're at home or out and doing things together, or even apart? Use A-Z if desired.

_____	_____	_____
_____	_____	_____
_____	_____	_____
_____	_____	_____
_____	_____	_____
_____	_____	_____
_____	_____	_____
_____	_____	_____
_____	_____	_____
_____	_____	_____
_____	_____	_____
_____	_____	_____
_____	_____	_____

What's it like to have an easy enjoyable relationship with each of my family members, even better than before? How does it feel when I close my eyes and imagine what it's like to be there and be living it? What's it like?

If desired, 1) Make note of anything you practiced in the past ten days that felt good to you and you wish to continue. 2) Add your favorite thought-provoking question and affirmation to the list you started.

If I am wanting things to feel even better at home, I'm going to create my own joy until others join me. I am now achieving an even more satisfying home life that supports my desire for total wellbeing. *Your turn*: I am
_____.

* * * * * * * * * * * * * * * * * * * *

What do you love about your home or family today and why?

_____
_____
_____
_____
_____

Intentions for My Day (Or tomorrow)

What words describe my day? I am feeling _____. I am being _____. I am having
_____. I am doing _____. How will I look and feel at the end of the day? Imagine it now.

More Appreciation & Intentions

What was my favorite part about today or this past week?

_____
_____
_____
_____
_____

What are three or more things I felt appreciation for and why?

_____
_____
_____
_____
_____
_____
_____

What are some things that happened at home that felt really good to me?

_____
_____
_____
_____
_____

I appreciate my home or family right now because...

_____
_____
_____
_____
_____
_____

Going forward, what ways do I intend to let myself enjoy my home or family life more and why are they good for me?

_____
_____
_____
_____
_____

If I continue putting my attention on my favorite things about each family member, I can work wonders. Thinking of the little things I appreciate about them minutes before I see them is a very effective way to allow our interactions to become better each time we see each other. It's like sending positive energy ahead of me. Try it for a couple weeks or so and see what you notice. Again, as I change how *I'm* thinking and acting and change my expectations about the way things will be for us, they change with me.

What do I love and appreciate most about each of my family members, whether they live with me or not? Or if preferred, what am I loving about my life right now?

_____

_____

_____

_____

_____

_____

_____

_____

_____

If desired, send out wishes for more joy and wellbeing to them or anyone you will see in the next 24 hours.

Intentions for the Days Ahead

What's my intention for this coming week or so? How do I expect things to go? What are all the words or phrases that describe it and how do I feel at the end of the week? If there's anything I wish to accomplish at home or elsewhere, what is it and how does it feel to have it done?

_____

_____

_____

_____

_____

_____

_____

Is anything inspiring me to be or have or do more of anything in particular? What is it and why do I want this?

_____

_____

_____

_____

Now, close your eyes and take about thirty seconds to visualize tomorrow and your week the way you want it to go from morning to night. See it and feel the ease and fun of it.

★ *First thing in the morning, ask:* "How do I wish to feel throughout my day today? I choose to feel _____."

Check-In & Set New Goals (if desired)

Have my wishes and dreams changed in the past few weeks? Let's go back to where this 100 day journey began. Do I recall how I was feeling then? Once again, read these questions from day 1 and notice if your desires have changed since then.

So how do I want my life to go? Where am I now, and where do I want to be? Do I wish to make any changes?

I'm going to write another wish list in a moment, but here are some things to consider, first.

> If I could have anything I want right now in this moment, what would I choose?
> In what ways do I wish to feel better than I do right now?
> Do I want more energy to do the things I love to do?
> Do I want to feel happier throughout my day?
> Do I want to feel more ease in my body?
> Do I want a clearer mind or to feel more peaceful?
> Do I want to make any changes in my body or health?
> Do I want to improve my relationships, and if so, in what way?
> Do I want to make changes in my work or social life?
> How would I feel after the changes?

How does it feel when I allow myself to feel the wellbeing flowing to me? Once again, take a moment and close your eyes and think of the things that you want for your overall wellbeing. Take yourself there and feel how it would feel to be living it. Stop reading and do this now.

Now you're ready to write out a new wish list.

A Wish List for Improving My Overall Wellbeing

Write the desired end result you want for the following areas:

My Health is: _____

My Mind is: _____

My Body looks and feels: _____

I am Feeling: _____

My Home and Family are: _____

My Relationship is: _____

My Work Life is: _____

My Personal Life is: _____

My Dreams and Plans are: _____

My Ideal Future is: _____

When I practice a state of wellbeing, it's a part of me and I believe in it. When I believe in my total wellbeing, I have an invincible mindset. I'm aligned with my natural-born energy of blissful wellbeing, and I do my best to *stay* aligned with it.

But every once in a while, I like to check in and see how I'm doing. And before I raise any question about it, I remind myself that I fully accept myself *wherever* I am. If I'm going to go there, I'm going to do it free of any pressure or guilt. *Always.* So, with a desire to maintain wellbeing, what kind of questions should I ask myself when checking in to see how I'm doing? What's the first one that comes to mind?

How about: what actions am I taking to keep moving forward? Have I made any changes in my life to help improve or maintain my health and happiness?

_____

What am I doing now in my daily routine to practice being more at ease?

_____

Have I created any *new* habits that inspire or cause me to feel more joy?

_____

Have I let go of any habits that no longer feel aligned with my desires or how I envision myself?

_____

How is my body feeling? Have there been any noticeable changes in how I feel?

_____

Am I feeling less stressed, if ever? Am I experiencing a calmer, clearer mind? Give an example.

_____

Have I been ignoring any needs or wants of my own? If so, what is something I can do to take a step toward change in that area, if desired?

_____

When a potentially stressful situation comes up, do I remember to focus on a solution rather than the problem? Give an example.

_____

What has my focused attention been on, primarily? And how am I doing at guiding or redirecting any unwanted thoughts?

_____

Next time I catch myself, I can say, "*I'm* in charge, mind, and I choose positive thoughts. Thank you for your cooperation." *Sounds pretty funny, doesn't it? But what if it works for you? You're in the process of retraining your mind to think how you want to think and allow you to feel how you want to feel. Yay*!

What do I believe about my current state of wellbeing or what's to come? What am I expecting?

_____

Am I giving myself credit when I notice how well I'm doing? Do I acknowledge or appreciate it in some way? What milestones, big or small, am I celebrating right now? I feel really good about:

_____

When I have the desire for blissful wellbeing, believe I can have it, and practice the feeling of it, it can become my reality. And the reason I'm practicing it until I've achieved it is because I know how good it feels. And I love feeling good. All day, every day.

A WISH Moment for Inspiration
Words Inspire Spiritual Harmony

If I want to feel my way into a state of blissful wellbeing, or just a state of *believing* that I can achieve blissful wellbeing, what kinds of things can I say to get myself there?

It's like I'm telling the story of how I wish it to be, but then I notice how natural it becomes for me to feel that way. So I tell myself something like this every single day:

I have such a strong immune system. My body and all its systems are functioning perfectly. I love my body and my body loves me. Body, thank you for the wellbeing. And thank you, to all my cells, for the wellbeing!

In the beginning I was saying it at the same time I did another habit so I wouldn't forget. Like during exercise or every time I got in or out of bed. With practice, I started thinking of it all the time. And that's how it took over any worrisome thought I ever had before. It's *fantastic*! And once I got this positive momentum going, I started thinking more positive thoughts like this:

I love being me. I love being in this body. I love living this life. I wouldn't want to be anyone else. I believe in myself. I feel the value of getting to be who I am. I love the way I think and feel. I love knowing what I know. I love that I cherish my thoughts and ideas. I love when I let myself revel in the spirit of joy. I love knowing that I can do anything.

I can choose how I want to feel. I can choose what I want to do. I get to choose what I believe and what I invite into my life. I can create any feeling and any reality I want to exist in. I am using my creative mind to be what I want to be. I can see it, feel it, taste it, and touch it, and it's mine.

I am now achieving blissful wellbeing. I love that I gave myself permission to feel as good as I deserve to feel and to know that is all I need to do to get to where I want to be!

My consistent thoughts and emotions are creating my reality. So I focus on the present joy that surrounds me and the joy of what's coming. I appreciate every part of it and know that's the key to attracting what I want. Why is it so easy for me to believe in my blissful wellbeing now?

♡♡♡ LOVE ~ PEACE ~ HARMONY ~ JOY ~ ABUNDANCE ~ FREEDOM ♡♡♡

Every one of these is now like the air I breathe. This is my powerful intention.

What are some other words I would like to say to myself or keep circulating in my mind? How about...

I have faith and trust that I am mentally strong and stable and my mind is achieving more...

_____

I have faith and trust that I am physically strong and stable and my body is achieving more...

_____

I have faith and trust that I'm going to continue to feel...

_____

I believe I can achieve...

_____

I am now aligning with more...

_____

My wellbeing gets easier to maintain every day because...

_____

I am taking actions and setting intentions to stay aligned with this, such as...

_____

And now allow the following questions to help you feel the reality that is available to you.

> Why am I feeling so certain that everything in my life is becoming better every day in every way?
> Why am I starting to feel so good?
> Why do I feel more at ease in my body now?
> What is making me feel lighter and brighter?
> When did I become so clear-minded?
> Why is it suddenly so easy for me to release unwanted thoughts and beliefs?
> Why am I able to be so mindful and present in nearly every moment now?
> How did I get to have so much more energy?
> How does it feel to allow myself to feel good all the time?
> When did I start feeling so focused and unstoppable in my spirit of peace and wellbeing?

All that I desire is flowing to me as I transform my thoughts.
All that I desire is flowing to me as I believe in my natural abilities.
All that I desire is flowing to me as I believe in my wellbeing.
And when I decide to achieve any goal and practice the feeling of what I want as though it's mine right now, it becomes so.

Improvement in all areas of your life is inevitable as you feel the emotions that come with your positive thoughts more consistently.

Here's an action step from Day 24 of _100 Days of Actions & Intentions to Create the Life You Wish For_:

It's time to breathe into your body with the intention to allow ease and replenish your energy.

As you breathe in, you'll be putting your attention on one part of the body and feeling energy pulling in there; as you breathe out more slowly, you're allowing the entire area to feel at ease and instantly release any tension.

Start by imagining there's a glowing ball of golden light in the space in front of your eyes. Begin _slowly_ breathing this energy into your face, exhale, and soften the entire face.

Take your time and continue energizing and softening as you breathe this golden light _in_ and out of each: the eyelids, cheeks, forehead, the entire face once again.

With your attention on your forehead again; _How much more pressure can I take off of my forehead?_ Breathe in. _How much more pressure can I feel lifting off of my head? How about my shoulders?_ Close your eyes and ask again.

And now breathe the light into your throat; exhale and soften your entire neck.

Now breathing the golden light into your chest, feel that it's the most blissful energy you've ever felt. Put your heartfelt effort into conjuring the feeling of it as though it's the first time you're seeing the sun in a very long time and you're breathing it in. It's soothing and energizing you and making you feel the fullness of your vitality.

How much better can you make it feel? Try it once more.

The most blissful energy you've ever felt is accessible. It's all around you. You're breathing it in right now, *evenly, slowly, lovingly.* Your body's breathing it in for you. You feel a lightness in your chest. There's no effort. Just a grand feeling of peace and pure elation.

Allow yourself to feel the self-love and acceptance that will enhance the flow of blissful energy you feel.

Gently but quickly breathe into the chest again, in 2–3 seconds, then slowly exhale and completely release all tension in the body. Softer.

Even softer. And now slowly breathing in, feel an extra layer of blissful energy washing over you and it's pouring into your heart center. Breathe into the chest again, and double the blissful energy and ease you feel now.

Now breathe it into your ribs and allow the ease to take over you.

Breathe into your abdomen and soften it completely as you exhale.

Breathing into your hips, energizing and softening more and more.

Then breathing light into your back and kidney area, and exhale, completely releasing any and all tension. Body, show me how it feels when I allow myself to feel blissful ease and wellbeing in my back. It's softer now, and energy is flowing there.

You're now experiencing an increase of circulation throughout your back, your body, and all your extremities. Your intention is doing this, along with your breath.

Continue breathing, energizing and softening your legs, your feet, and come back up to your arms, the palms of your hands, and once more to your face. Intend to breathe in and out at each area.

Breathing into your body now, you feel blissful energy washing over you, and it's pouring into every cell of your body. As you exhale, your entire body relaxes. Settle your attention on your heart center now and thank your body for the blissful wellbeing it continues to show you each and every day.

Body, how much lighter and freer can I feel, now and in the minutes and hours to follow? Show me how it feels.

Give yourself a moment to relax and feel the energy. Try closing your eyes and breathing into your face, chest, and abdomen once more, if desired. It may help you feel the energy more.

If desired, you can practice using a hand mudra during your daily meditation or breathing exercise, or any time you're sitting down to relax. Avoid doing this any time you have a cold or cough. Rest the back of your hands next to you or on your legs and place them in the Prana mudra position; with the tip of the thumb touching the tip of the ring and little finger, and keep the index and middle finger straight and gently extended.

Simply put, the Prana mudra is felt to energize the body. It recharges the inactive energy in the body, and is said to promote healing of over a hundred disorders. It is felt to restore balance, increase longevity, clarity and confidence, and relieve fatigue and depression.

Amazingly, it's also said to help correct vitamin deficiencies, impurities in the blood, and improve eye health. Just imagine what else it can do. And mudras have been practiced for so long, its origin is considered prehistoric.

The fingers used in this mudra connect the earth, water, and fire elements of the body and stimulate the root chakra (one of seven main energy centers of the body) at the base of the spine. This generates heat that awakens the organs and revitalizes the body's energy.

To achieve the best results, practice the mudra daily for a minimum of fifteen minutes and up to 45 minutes, while sitting or walking or lying down. It's also important to stay tuned in to your breath.

Do your best to hold the belief that you're able to free yourself of any struggle and achieve blissful wellbeing on a daily basis. If not now, in time you will. Allow yourself to feel the pure positive energy and wellbeing that is available and continually flowing to you.

Always follow your intuition and find ways that work best for you, for all of these practices. The answers that are right for you are *all* within you. The more quiet time you spend with yourself, the more you will hear any insights that are uniquely beneficial to you.

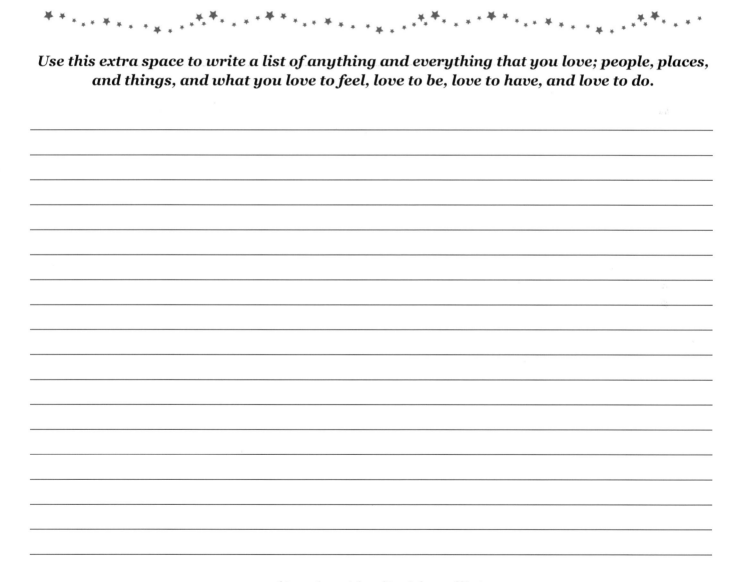

Use this extra space to write a list of anything and everything that you love; people, places, and things, and what you love to feel, love to be, love to have, and love to do.

_____
_____
_____
_____
_____
_____
_____
_____
_____
_____
_____
_____
_____
_____
_____
_____
_____
_____

★ I Am More Aligned With Blissful Wellbeing Every Day

For the next ten days, the topic will mainly be on what you wrote on Day 1 as your desired end result for...

My Relationship is: _____. Please fill it in once again. How much more can I enhance the relationship with myself or with my partner in a way that supports my wellbeing?

Write a letter to your current partner or an ideal partner you are now inviting into your life. If you prefer to be single, write to your deeply satisfying single life, or anything you wish. As if they were sitting right in front of you, tell them; 1) What you want the relationship to be like between you. 2) How you would like them to feel when they're with you. 3) How you would like to feel when you're with them, and 4) Why you want this. Don't skip any of these points and add some of your own. Pour your heart out.

Dear Partner, Soulmate, or Amazing Single Life,

_____

_____

_____

_____

_____

_____

_____

_____

_____

_____

_____

_____

_____

_____

_____

_____

_____

_____

_____

_____

I am now aligning with the energy of my ideal relationship. *Your turn*: I am _____.

Intentions for My Day (Or tomorrow)

What words describe my day? I am feeling _____. I am being _____. I am having _____. I am doing _____. How will I look and feel at the end of the day? Imagine it now.

Part of my total wellbeing is to be in a healthy and happy relationship, if desired, and feel completely worthy of it. I want it to feel right, and that begins with feeling good about myself. When I treat myself well, others follow my lead.

And I always find creative ways to attract the right partner or nurture and improve the relationship I'm in. First I decide what kind of relationship I want and how I want it to feel when I'm in it. And then I think of the qualities I want my partner to have and whether or not I'm giving out the vibe that will attract those qualities.

I can easily attract what my energy is aligned with. I can do this by feeling as though it's already done. As I change my perception about any relationship, my energy changes and the circumstances must change with me.

Whether I'm with my current partner or wishing to meet an ideal partner, what kind of relationship do I want to have with them? What does it look and feel like? I want to focus on this desired end result. This is what it's like:

We are spending more time talking about...

_____

_____

When we're together, we are feeling...

_____

Physical activities we like to do together are...

_____

_____

We both started caring more about...

_____

_____

We are feeling more comfortable about...

_____

_____

I am feeling more connected to them because...

_____

We are being...

_____

_____

We are having more fun doing...

_____

_____

We are doing more of what I wish to do. We are...

_____

_____

We are totally in sync about...

_____

_____

Our life feels even better because...

_____

Additionally, our life has changed in the following ways:

_____

_____

_____

_____

I am now attuning to the harmony of an even greater relationship. *Your turn*: I am _____.

**What do you love most about your current relationship or the
idea of meeting someone and why?**

_____

_____

_____

_____

_____

_____

_____

_____

_____

_____

_____

Intentions for My Day (Or tomorrow)

What words describe my day? I am feeling _____. I am being _____. I am having
_____. I am doing _____. How will I look and feel at the end of the day? Imagine it now.

I have the ability to attract the relationship I want or transform the one I'm in until it feels just right for me. What does a healthy and happy relationship mean to me?

_____

To set myself up for success in achieving this, I do what I can to let go of any leftover feelings about past relationships. What if I'm repeating the same kind of relationship patterns because I was thinking of all the parts I didn't like about them and that's what I've been attracting? If I look at those I've left behind with appreciation in some way, I'll bring that positive energy into the relationship I'm in or *will* be in.

If you're comfortable with it, write a list of one or more things you liked about each longer relationship you've been in. What were the best parts? What are my favorite things about each of them that I would love in my current or next relationship?

_____	_____	_____
_____	_____	_____
_____	_____	_____
_____	_____	_____
_____	_____	_____
_____	_____	_____
_____	_____	_____

As I focus on what I like best about my relationship or the person I am becoming aligned with, I become a magnet for the partner or better relationship I want. Do I feel happy where I am and have faith in it happening? What else do I think would help me believe in the wonderful relationship that's available to me, no matter how it seems now?

_____

What is going really well for us now or with my dating or single life?

_____

_____

Our strengths are...

_____

I feel happiest when we are...

_____

I think they feel happiest when we are...

_____

The habits or activities we enjoy that support our happiness are...

_____

_____

The habits or activities that are not feeling right and might be best for us to stop doing, if desired, are...

_____

I want to appreciate each other more so that when we're together we are more...

_____

I want to communicate even better than we do now so that we can talk about things that matter like...

_____

I would like the courage to ask them to...

_____

I want to be more myself with them so that I let them see the side of me that's...

_____

In some ways I'd like things to lighten up between us so that we can...

_____

If I had a magic wand, what changes would I make for us right now?

_____

_____

How would this change our relationship or our life together?

_____

I believe it's achievable because...

_____

I am feeling happy, healthy, and worthy, and therefore attracting a happy, healthy relationship. Today and in the days ahead, I am achieving an atmosphere for success in having the kind of relationship I wish for. _Your turn_: I am _____.

What do you love about where your relationship or single/dating life is headed and why?

_____

_____

_____

Intentions for My Day (Or tomorrow)

What words describe my day? I am feeling _____. I am being _____. I am having _____. I am doing _____. How will I look and feel at the end of the day? Imagine it now.

Today is about allowing your desired relationship to come along more easily. Something fun that you can try is to daydream about your ideal relationship whenever the mood strikes. It can help you get in the feeling place of being in it, and that much closer to living it. Imagine how it feels to be with them, what you're doing together, what you would talk about, where you'd go, and what you're planning for your weekend or your next trip. Write out the details of something you would like to daydream about.

_____

_____

_____

_____

_____

_____

_____

_____

_____

_____

If it feels good, do it as often as you like. Whether it's to improve the current relationship you're in or attract someone new, you're getting ready for it. You're talking yourself into it. You're feeling good about it.

You're not missing someone or waiting for them; you're feeling *just right* where you are and excited about what's to come. You're feeling worthy and know the value you offer that *lucky* someone.

If you're ever hurting over a breakup, do your best to think of it in a way that allows you to feel better. Something like this: they couldn't handle the responsibility of a relationship. And the best part is, I'm free to meet the "right" someone. If I was still with the wrong someone, I would miss the one that's lining up for me. My ideal partner and I are becoming ready for each other. I appreciate all those who came before "the right one," for they helped me know what I truly wanted and deserved in a relationship.

Now and in the days ahead, I am achieving an atmosphere for success in having an even better relationship. *Your turn*: I am _____.

How are you feeling today and why do you think that is?
If you think you could feel even better, what are the words that would describe it?
Breathe in the meaning of each word as it's written.

_____

_____

_____

_____

Intentions for My Day (Or tomorrow)

What words describe my day? I am feeling _____. I am being _____. I am having _____. I am doing _____. How will I look and feel at the end of the day? Imagine it now.

Today is about practicing the feeling place of having the relationship I want. There's no limit to how happy our relationship can be. How does it feel to be "the one" that's going to attract my ideal partner? Or reignite the relationship I'm in? I am their "one," and they are mine. Ideally, I want to feel happy with who I am and where we are, yet feel the possibility of what we can become. It can become the way I imagined it, or even better. Once again, I'm going to answer these questions based on how I *want* my relationship to be:

What is our ideal relationship like?

_____

_____

_____

Do I feel confident and happy, and do I act that way when I'm with my partner?

_____

When I'm with them, what are the words that describe how I feel?

_____

How do we treat each other?

_____

_____

What does it feel like when we're being kind and respectful? Or when we playfully tease each other? Imagine how it would feel. How do I prefer things to be between us?

_____

_____

What are some things we like to talk about?

_____

_____

_____

What activities do we like to do together or apart?

_____

_____

_____

What plans are we making? What will we do on weekends? Where do we like to go together on vacation?

_____

_____

_____

_____

What kinds of things do we do for each other? Think of three things each of us enjoy doing for each other.

_____

_____

_____

What is my favorite quality about them?

_____

How do they make me feel when I'm with them and what do I love about it?

_____

Am I being my genuine self with them? How am I letting them in? Am I able to tell them how I really feel?

_____

If I could sum it up in one sentence, how am I acting and feeling when I'm magnetic to my ideal partner?

_____

Notice if you feel any differently than before when you think of your partner or ideal partner. Close your eyes a moment and imagine what it's like when your relationship is how you wish it to be, or even better. See the two of you laughing and doing something you enjoy. Write any words or phrases you can think of that would describe what it's like. I love how good I feel when we're fully enjoying each other like this. It feels like...

_____   _____

_____   _____

_____   _____

_____   _____

_____   _____

_____   _____

What is my favorite part about having this come true and why? If it feels good to think of this, do it often. I am better every day at guiding my thoughts and emotions to align with the energy of my ideal relationship. *Your turn*: I am _____. Why is this starting to feel so much easier to do?

What are you loving and appreciating about yourself right now and why?
How about your day?

_____

_____

_____

Intentions for My Day (Or tomorrow)

What words describe my day? I am feeling _____. I am being _____. I am having _____. I am doing _____. How will I look and feel at the end of the day? Imagine it now.

Day 56 _____

It's time to take the next obvious step toward my goal. What actions can I take that I believe will help me achieve an even happier relationship or provide an opportunity to meet someone? Write a list of habits or activities that I could participate in or my partner and I could do together that I believe will bring us closer together. What have I been wanting to do with them or for them, or do more often? And what have they mentioned to me?

_____ _____ _____
_____ _____ _____
_____ _____ _____
_____ _____ _____
_____ _____ _____
_____ _____ _____
_____ _____ _____
_____ _____ _____
_____ _____ _____
_____ _____ _____
_____ _____ _____
_____ _____ _____
_____ _____ _____
_____ _____ _____

Circle those that feel the most satisfying and consider picking a date each week or month or so to make it happen.

I am feeling more inspired every day to find ways to have more fun with my partner or on my own. *Your turn:* I am_____.

Which activity feels the most fun or satisfying to think about and why?
And which do you intend to do first and why?

_____
_____
_____
_____
_____

Intentions for My Day (Or tomorrow)

What words describe my day? I am feeling _____. I am being _____. I am having _____. I am doing _____. How will I look and feel at the end of the day? Imagine it now.

It's time to practice my belief and expectation of things working out for me and my relationship in the best possible way. It will be just as I imagined, or even better. And all in perfect timing.

I trust that things are working out for us because...

_____

_____

My favorite part of our relationships is...

_____

_____

_____

_____

The best time we ever had was...

_____

_____

I believe there are more good times coming and things working out for us like...

_____

_____

_____

_____

Here's what else I see for us in the years to come...

_____

_____

_____

I expect things to continue going well for us because...

_____

_____

I am really looking forward to...

_____

_____

I am ready for...

_____

_____

I believe we are now achieving...

_____

_____

_____

If it was happening right now and I felt how I wanted to feel and was having the kind of day I would love to have every day with my partner or ideal partner, what would we be doing right now? Where would we be? What are we talking about or planning to do? How would I be feeling?

_____

_____

_____

_____

_____

_____

How is having the kind of relationship I want affecting my overall wellbeing? In what way is it benefiting my mind, body, and spirit?

_____

_____

_____

_____

I am holding the vision of this in my mind and letting go of the how. I am open and receptive to whatever way it unfolds. *Your turn*: I am _____.

What part of your desired outcome do you believe in most and why?
Do your best to focus on this part of it, and anything that seems unchangeable can transform more easily.

_____

_____

_____

_____

_____

_____

_____

Intentions for My Day (Or tomorrow)

What words describe my day? I am feeling _____. I am being _____. I am having _____. I am doing _____. How will I look and feel at the end of the day? Imagine it now.

This is my day of solutions. In regards to my current relationship or the one I wish to find, what would it take for me to be ready for the relationship I see myself in? Do I feel open and receptive to it now? Do I hear a resounding "Yes!"? If single, does it feel like my life has room for two? Is there a place for them? If my partner or ideal mate could speak to me now and tell me what they want from me and how they want things to be between us, what do I think they'd say? Think it through before answering.

_____

_____

_____

_____

_____

_____

_____

_____

_____

_____

How do I feel about that?

_____

_____

_____

How does it feel to know that the more I love and accept myself, the more I attract the relationship I want and the more comfortable and enjoyable it is to be in the relationship?

If I want to feel ready for when I meet someone new, I can think of what I'd say when I meet them. If they were sitting across from me right now, and I was feeling as brave as ever, what would I say to them? Think of one question and two statements that would get a conversation going and show them the most genuine part of me.

_____

_____

_____

My true self is the part of me they won't be able to resist, and they can't wait to see me again! How does it feel to be *so* confident that I say what I want to say the moment I want to say it, even if it's to someone I'm attracted to? It doesn't seem so scary anymore!

And if I'm in a relationship now, what if I started wishing them more joy, laughter, love, and wellbeing before I see them each day? What if it works so well that it completely transforms our relationship to an even greater level of happiness for both of us? This is entirely possible, as it has worked for others. Am I willing to try it every day until I see the results? I intend to give it my best try! What are my wishes for them? I wish you more...

_____

How has my life changed afterward? How do we feel when we're together? If I close my eyes right now I can take myself there and be in the feeling place of it. How good does it feel? Where are we and what are we doing? What are we laughing about? Imagine it now.

Is there anything else going on that I wish to find a positive solution for, whether it's about a relationship or something else? If desired, think of what it is and then focus on how I want things to be. Use present tense to describe how things turn out.

_____

_____

_____

_____

_____

How would it feel to have this situation be really comfortable for me?

_____

_____

What are the words to describe how I feel when a better outcome is taking place?

_____

_____

What are the words to describe how I feel afterward?

_____

_____

I have the ability to see everything in a way that benefits my relationship and my wellbeing. I am freeing myself of any concerns that I have no control over. I am focused on what I *can* control, which is how I feel. I choose to feel good and see things in a positive way. I like believing that all is well with us and getting better every day in every way. *Your turn*: I am _____.

What do you love about your current mindset around your relationship or single life and why?

_____

_____

_____

_____

_____

_____

_____

Intentions for My Day (Or tomorrow)

What words describe my day? I am feeling _____. I am being _____. I am having _____. I am doing _____. How will I look and feel at the end of the day? Imagine it now.

Think of the current relationship I'm in or the person I want to attract and what qualities I believe will attract them to me. What do I think they would be? It's however I feel when I am being true to my authentic nature. How do I see myself in my truest form? I am irresistible to my partner or soul mate in this form. It's who I am *now*. What are these qualities? Write a list of them and how you look and feel and act when you are living and breathing it, loving and owning it. Use A-Z, if desired.

_____   _____   _____
_____   _____   _____
_____   _____   _____
_____   _____   _____
_____   _____   _____
_____   _____   _____
_____   _____   _____
_____   _____   _____

Now list all the qualities that you want in your ideal partner, including their lifestyle, personality, career goals, looks, height, age, and more. And if you're already in a relationship, list all your favorite things about them: favorite attributes, things they do for you, how they make you feel, or anything you can think of that you cherish about them or wish to experience with them.

_____   _____   _____
_____   _____   _____
_____   _____   _____
_____   _____   _____
_____   _____   _____
_____   _____   _____
_____   _____   _____
_____   _____   _____

When I focus on what I appreciate or my favorite things about them, my wishes for an even happier relationship can begin to magically take place. *Important note* - if I think of all my favorite things about them before I'm about to see them, it can work wonders. *Try it for a while and notice how much better you start to get along, even better than before.*

Another weird but fun way to use this game is to use A–Z to create a name for the many soulmates that are available to you, and state one or more qualities that each of them have. An example for letter A is "Alex/Alexis is adorable, affluent, and articulate." When all 26 of their qualities are combined, you've created the ideal partner for you. Hooray! Then you can hold this intention and vision as your expectation for the next relationship you're in, if applicable. Have fun with this. It really can get you thinking and expecting that your perfect *someone* is going to walk right up to you. And they will, *somewhere*, sometime. Think of it while you're walking or driving, and write it out now. Just keep thinking that *anything* is possible.

A. _____
B. _____
C. _____
D. _____
E. _____
F. _____
G. _____
H. _____
I. _____
J. _____
K. _____
L. _____
M. _____
N. _____
O. _____
P. _____
Q. _____
R. _____
S. _____
T. _____
U. _____
V. _____
W. _____
X. _____
Y. _____
Z. _____

How much more radiant and magnetic to my ideal mate am I able to feel right now? *If desired, slow your breath and feel as though you're breathing a beautiful, radiant energy into your face and chest. Close your eyes, ask again, and allow your body to respond.*

If desired, 1) Make note of anything you practiced in the past ten days that felt good to you and you wish to continue. 2) Add your favorite thought-provoking question and affirmation to the list you started.

If I'm wanting to feel magnetic to the relationship I want, I'm going to be my radiant self wherever I go. I am as irresistible as I believe I am. I am now achieving a healthier relationship or the dating life or fun single life that supports my desire for total wellbeing. *Your turn*: I am_____.

Intentions for My Day (Or tomorrow)

What words describe my day? I am feeling _____. I am being _____. I am having _____. I am doing _____. How will I look and feel at the end of the day? Imagine it now.

More Appreciation & Intentions

What was my favorite part about today or this past week? Can I recall any great conversations or laughter with my partner, family, colleagues, or friends? Am I feeling good about any goals or tasks I accomplished?

_____

_____

_____

_____

What are three or more things I felt appreciation for and why?

_____

_____

_____

_____

I appreciate myself for how much I am allowing myself to go with the flow and feel more at ease in the following ways: At home, I am...

_____

_____

_____

With my partner, I am...

_____

_____

_____

At work, I am...

_____

_____

_____

With my friends, I am...

_____

_____

_____

In my personal time, I am...

_____

_____

_____

What else do I appreciate about my partner or ideal partner? What do I wish for them or just want them to know? If I imagine they're sitting in front of me right now, and I had no fear of how they'd respond, what would I love for them to know?

_____

_____

_____

_____

_____

_____

How much more am I able to let myself enjoy my relationship? How much more am I able to focus on what I love about it? This is the key to allowing us to grow together.

Intentions for the Days Ahead

What's my intention for this coming week or so? How do I expect things to go? What are all the words or phrases that describe it and how do I feel at the end of the week?

_____

_____

_____

_____

_____

_____

_____

_____

_____

_____

What is inspiring me to enjoy my own time or time with my partner more?

_____

What am I looking forward to today or tomorrow?

_____

What am I looking forward to most for this coming week or weekend?

_____

If desired, send out wishes for more joy and wellbeing to anyone I will see today or tomorrow. What do I wish for them?

_____

Now, close your eyes and take about thirty seconds to visualize tomorrow and your week the way you want it to go from morning to night. Feel the joy of it.

★ _First thing in the morning, ask:_ "How do I wish to feel throughout my day today? I choose to feel _____."

For the next ten days, the topic will mainly be on what you wrote on Day 1 as your desired end result for...

My Work Life: _____. Please fill it in once again. Does the work you do feel like your life purpose? If not, would you like it to be, or are you content where you are? Is it easy to leave work behind and focus on your family or personal life? Or perhaps you're not working but enjoy some hobbies. Base the next ten days on whichever is your preference.

Imagine you're having a conversation with a symbol that represents your workplace or life purpose. Speak to the satisfaction of the workplace you're at or to the desire for a better environment there. Or speak to your life purpose, as in your ideal dream job or the work you're doing now that you love. Tell it what you want, why you want it, and how it will benefit you and your state of wellbeing when you have it. Fill the page with as many details as possible.

Dear Purpose,

_____
_____
_____
_____
_____
_____
_____
_____
_____
_____
_____
_____
_____
_____
_____
_____
_____
_____
_____
_____
_____

I am now aligning with my desire for an even more satisfying work life. *Your turn*: I am

_____.

Intentions for My Day (Or tomorrow)

What words describe my day? I am feeling _____. I am being _____. I am having _____. I am doing _____. How will I look and feel at the end of the day? Imagine it now.

Day 62 _____

It's important to keep my desired end result in mind for how I want my ideal work life to be. Once I've achieved this, what am I doing differently? How do I think I would be acting and feeling?

I am spending more time thinking about...

_____

I am feeling...

_____

I am feeling more confident and connected to my life purpose or ideal future because...

_____

I am being...

_____

I am having more fun doing...

_____

I am doing more of what I wish to do. I am...

_____

My life feels better because I am...

_____

I have more time to...

_____

Additionally, my life has changed in the following ways:

_____

I am now aligning with the energy of my ideal work life. *Your turn*: I am _____.

What do you love most about your current work and why?

_____

_____

_____

Intentions for My Day (Or tomorrow)

What words describe my day? I am feeling _____. I am being _____. I am having _____. I am doing _____. How will I look and feel at the end of the day? Imagine it now.

I decided to align with the kind of work I absolutely love to do or enjoy what I do in the best possible way. What does my ideal work life or life purpose mean to me?

_____

_____

_____

If not already, how do I get there? To begin with, I am creating an atmosphere for success in achieving it. I am practicing what I can do to allow it to flow into my life. Does it feel like anything needs to happen in order for me to align with this?

_____

What is going really well for me in relation to my current work or a career I'm working toward?

_____

_____

_____

_____

My greatest achievements are...

_____

_____

I feel that I support my wellbeing in how I go about doing my work in the following ways...

_____

_____

The parts I don't feel right about, if any, and hope to change are...

_____

_____

I also wish to improve on...

_____

_____

I feel the most satisfied with my work when I am...

_____

_____

I feel the most productive when I...

_____

_____

If I had a magic wand, what changes would I make to my work life?

_____

_____

_____

How would this affect me in the year ahead?

_____

_____

I believe it's achievable because...

_____

_____

What state of mind do I think I need to be in to achieve it? What are some new thoughts I could practice to align with the energy of my ideal work life?

_____

_____

_____

_____

If my ideal work life or life purpose could speak to me, what would it tell me? It's telling me what it will do for me and what it wants *me* to do for it. What would it say? (Keep in mind, it wants me as much as I want it!)

_____

_____

_____

_____

_____

_____

I am now achieving an atmosphere for success in achieving this desire. *Your turn*: I am

_____.

What do you love about the direction your work life is headed in and why?

_____

_____

_____

Intentions for My Day (Or tomorrow)

What words describe my day? I am feeling _____. I am being _____. I am having _____. I am doing _____. How will I look and feel at the end of the day? Imagine it now.

Since work can sometimes be stressful, my ultimate goal is to fully believe in my ability to protect my positive energy and stay in a good-feeling place no matter what's happening around me. What is something I can do each morning that sets me up for a great day? Some ideas are journaling, meditation, yoga, qi gong, an energy protection routine, or setting intentions. *If not already, make a plan below for your next work day. If it feels good, continue the routine. Give it time and you may notice the positive results by the way you feel throughout your day.*

When I wake up I intend to enjoy a few minutes or more of...

_____

Before my day begins, I consciously make a choice by setting these intentions for how my day will go...

_____

_____

My morning routine also includes:

_____

_____

I feel thankful in advance for my day going as I expected, or better. By the time I leave for work I am feeling...

_____

During my ride to work, if applicable, I send these good thoughts out for/to...

_____

_____

If I set intentions again midday and throughout my day, it will create the results I'm asking for more easily. How do I want my afternoon to go?

_____

_____

To feel more joyful and present at work, I intend to...

_____

_____

I am practicing thoughts throughout my day that make me feel...

_____

When something potentially stressful comes up, I can use a ready-made phrase or affirmation to remind me of my ability to stay in a good-feeling place, such as "I choose wellbeing." If desired, I could then take a cleansing breath to exhale any tension, followed by a deep breath and imagine I'm breathing in blissful wellbeing. What will be my phrase to help in stressful moments throughout my day? What energy will I be breathing in? Do I have a favorite word or affirmation? Or what other ways have I found that work for me?

_____

_____

How do I want my evenings to go? And what can I do before I get home to wind down or feel ready to enjoy time with my family or partner before I walk in the door, if desired?

_____

_____

_____

Additionally, when I have an upcoming event, I can improve the outcome by practicing how I want it to go. For instance, before a job interview or requesting a raise, I can imagine being there and seeing it go well, and hearing them offer the salary and other benefits I'd like, or seeing it in writing on a document. Then imagine receiving the email or phone call giving me the good news and how it feels to hear it. Does anything like this come to mind? Go through the steps of the whole experience and write out the details.

_____

_____

_____

_____

_____

What are the words of encouragement I need to gain the confidence to see something like this through?

_____

Take your time, close your eyes and ask, "Inner guidance, what would you tell me to think or say or do in this situation?" Did you receive any insight? What was it?

_____

_____

_____

Use this process any time you want answers for anything. You'll often be amazed at the answers that come through and the clarity or objectivity you suddenly have to see yourself or a situation more clearly.

I am ready for anything that life brings my way. I am in control of my emotions and armed with intentions. Anything that presents as a potential issue doesn't last long. It never has a chance to. I know what to do. *Your turn*: I am _____.

What is one favorite thing you enjoy thinking about that always lifts you up?
What do you love about it and how does it make you feel specifically?

_____

_____

_____

Intentions for My Day (Or tomorrow)

What words describe my day? I am feeling _____. I am being _____. I am having _____. I am doing _____. How will I look and feel at the end of the day? Imagine it now.

Remember, where your attention goes, energy flows. So focusing on what you like about the work you do will help bring that positive energy into your next experience, if applicable. You're inviting more good work experiences into your future. With that in mind, write a list of what you appreciate about your work and perhaps your favorite part of any work you've done in the past. Include your favorite people, places, opportunities, creative moments, tasks, projects, productivity, results, what you've gained, or anything you can think of.

_____   _____
_____   _____
_____   _____
_____   _____
_____   _____
_____   _____
_____   _____
_____   _____
_____   _____

Now think about your ideal work, whether it's one of your dreams or plans or could be an improvement in what you're doing now. What would you be doing? How does it feel to be there and be doing the kind of work you would truly love to be doing? Close your eyes and take yourself there. Then write the words or phrases that describe what you were doing and how it felt.

_____   _____
_____   _____
_____   _____
_____   _____
_____   _____
_____   _____
_____   _____
_____   _____
_____   _____

I am ready to let this happen because...

_____
_____
_____

Having this desire is changing my life by...

_____
_____
_____

This is making my life easier by...

_____
_____
_____

What are the words or phrases that describe how it feels when I'm living my life with these changes? What's different at work or home or in my personal life?

_____   _____
_____   _____
_____   _____
_____   _____
_____   _____
_____   _____
_____   _____
_____   _____
_____   _____

See yourself happily doing the work with ease or spending time doing what you wish. My life is now transforming to accommodate my every wish. *Your turn*: I am _____. Why is it becoming so easy for me to feel this way now?

What are you loving and appreciating about yourself or your day or life right now and why?

_____
_____
_____
_____
_____
_____
_____
_____
_____
_____
_____

Intentions for My Day (Or tomorrow)

What words describe my day? I am feeling _____. I am being _____. I am having _____. I am doing _____. How will I look and feel at the end of the day? Imagine it now.

It's time to take the next obvious step toward my goal for a higher level of joy and wellbeing. Whether I want to improve my current work situation, move forward on a side project, start a new hobby, or line up a whole new career, right now I can write a list of action steps or new habits that I want to take when I'm ready. If I set aside some time, what would I love to learn, research, or take action on that will bring me closer to my desired end result? If the thought of something excites me, it's the right move.

_____	_____	_____
_____	_____	_____
_____	_____	_____
_____	_____	_____
_____	_____	_____
_____	_____	_____
_____	_____	_____
_____	_____	_____
_____	_____	_____
_____	_____	_____
_____	_____	_____
_____	_____	_____
_____	_____	_____
_____	_____	_____

Going forward, I am taking time for baby steps or big steps toward my best life. *Your turn*: I am
_____.

Which activity feels the most fun or satisfying to think about and why?
And which do you intend to do first and why?

_____
_____
_____
_____
_____
_____

Intentions for My Day (Or tomorrow)

What words describe my day? I am feeling _____. I am being _____. I am having _____. I am doing _____. How will I look and feel at the end of the day? Imagine it now.

It's time to practice my belief and expectation of things working out for me. Remember, what I believe I can be, I can achieve. What am I primarily thinking about? When I focus on what I enjoy most about the work I do, envision how I want it to be, and look forward to what's to come, I am lining myself up with the absolute best work experience for me.

When it comes to my current work situation, I believe things can become even better because...

_____

_____

When it comes to my future work situation, I believe...

_____

_____

_____

I believe I am better every day at...

_____

_____

_____

The greatest thing that could happen right now is...

_____

_____

_____

_____

The greatest thing that I expect to happen with my work in the next couple years is...

_____

_____

_____

_____

I am excited and ready for...

_____

_____

_____

_____

I trust that things are working out for me because...

_____

_____

_____

I feel limitless in my ability to achieve...

_____

_____

_____

_____

If it was happening right now and I felt how I wanted to feel and was having the kind of work day I would love to have every day, what would it be like? What am I doing and how am I feeling from morning to night, before, during, and after work? What do I love about it?

_____

_____

_____

_____

_____

_____

_____

_____

_____

_____

_____

_____

_____

_____

_____

_____

I believe in my ability to achieve anything I decide to do. I am holding the vision of it in my mind and letting go of the how, and I feel free. I am open and receptive to all the gifts the universe has in store for me. *Your turn*: I am _____.

How much more are you able to believe in your ability to achieve an even better work environment or whatever your desired outcome is? *What part of it do you believe in most and why?*

_____

_____

_____

_____

Intentions for My Day (Or tomorrow)

What words describe my day? I am feeling _____. I am being _____. I am having _____. I am doing _____. How will I look and feel at the end of the day? Imagine it now.

This is our day for positive solutions. The goal this week is to find ways to enjoy my work even more than I have before and in a way that supports my wellbeing. What kind of solutions do I need for my work life?

Is there anything I can think of that I'm occasionally confronted with that feels uncomfortable? Something I would *love* to speak up about or quickly smooth over if it happens again?

_____

_____

What outcome do I want and what steps can I take in that direction?

_____

_____

Do I need to arm myself with a blanket statement to be prepared when someone's unkind words take me off guard? What would that sound like? Could I smile and tell them I'll respond when they speak kindly? Eeks! That might not go over so well at work. But I could say...

_____

_____

How do I confidently ask for something I want? I want to offer words that are so kindly or wisely put that they *cannot* be denied. How do I convey my words with expectation for a positive response and get one?

_____

_____

_____

_____

Could I visualize how I want things to be and be in the qualities and energy of the desired outcome? Take a moment and imagine watching the incident go from potentially stressful to easy-peasy. I offer a gentle, soft-spoken and respectful response or instruction, yet I come through with a confident and commanding presence, and the expectation is clear and undeniable. And so am I! How does it feel to have it go my way?

_____

_____

This person wants to respond to me as kindly, or confidently as I did, or at least appear to. See the end result: a shaking of hands, a hug, or a better work environment. Whatever it is that I want this situation to be like going forward, see it now. Play it through in the mind's eye once again.

How does it feel to be influencing the outcome the next time it happens, if ever? What's it like to have that feeling of satisfaction after I've achieved a better relationship with the person?

_____

_____

What if I knew the person would never again approach me in that way? What a wonderful feeling to have gained newfound respect from someone just for speaking up for myself in the kindest, gentlest way.

I also like to keep in mind that I'm in charge of how I feel and how I react to things. Feeling good is more important to me now because:

_____

_____

I can even improve potentially stressful situations by focusing on what I admire or appreciate about it, or about the people involved. What is my favorite part about it? If I can see it in a different way or find something to appreciate about it, it could change the circumstances altogether. My favorite thing about a recent incident with a person or situation is...

_____

_____

_____

When I respond positively to a stressful situation with kindness, respect, patience, or tolerance, others tend to follow my lead. Any time I change the way I usually respond to someone or a situation, it will automatically create a change in the outcome. And every interaction thereafter will feel better and easier.

Although I may not accept or like what's happening at times, it may not even be about me. What I put my focused attention on will get bigger. So if I resist it or let it frustrate me for long, more things like it can show up. Therefore, I choose to put my focus on how I prefer things to be or turn my attention to something else, such as:

_____

_____

I am always open to finding more ways to enjoy my work. I want to enjoy my work because...

_____

_____

_____

I have faith in my ability to cope with any stress that comes my way. Not only getting by, but handling it brilliantly. I let my creativity fly when it comes to finding the best ways to gracefully maneuver my way through life and the many personalities and situations that come with it.

If not now, there will come a day when I look at everything with an eye for the potential positive outcome it offers me. *Your turn*: I am _____.

What do you love most about your current mindset around your work and why?

_____

_____

_____

Intentions for My Day (Or tomorrow)

What words describe my day? I am feeling _____. I am being _____. I am having _____. I am doing _____. How will I look and feel at the end of the day? Imagine it now.

What are the qualities or energy that I'm in or intend to be in to enjoy my work life or home projects more? What's it like to have a great experience at work or with home projects every day? When I'm feeling creative, inspired, motivated, productive, or optimistic every morning and letting it carry me through my day, what's it like to live that way? And how do I feel at the end of the day when everything's gone my way, easily and effortlessly? What are the many words or phrases that would describe it? *Include every detail about what you're doing, how you feel when you're doing it, and how your success is affecting your life.*

_____   _____   _____
_____   _____   _____
_____   _____   _____
_____   _____   _____
_____   _____   _____
_____   _____   _____
_____   _____   _____
_____   _____   _____
_____   _____   _____
_____   _____   _____
_____   _____   _____

How does it feel to close my eyes right now and imagine what it's like to be there and be living it? How did it feel?

_____

Going forward, I am doing my best to practice being one with this energy. I am living and breathing it.

If desired, 1) Make note of anything you practiced in the past ten days that felt good to you if you would like to continue the practice. 2) Add your favorite thought-provoking question and affirmation to our list. And 3) Reminder to ask yourself daily, "How does it feel when I allow myself to feel blissful?" I am now achieving a more satisfying work life that supports my desire for total wellbeing. *Your turn*: I am_____.

Imagine it's a couple months from now and you're telling someone about your success at work or how much better it's been for you. *What would you tell them? Additionally, put something in their hand that symbolizes a part of it, such as a photograph or finished product of what you've been working on. What is it?*

_____
_____
_____

Intentions for My Day (Or tomorrow)

What words describe my day? I am feeling _____. I am being _____. I am having _____. I am doing _____. How will I look and feel at the end of the day? Imagine it now.

More Appreciation & Intentions

What was my favorite part about today or this past week? Am I feeling good about any goals or tasks I accomplished?

_____

_____

_____

What are three or more things I felt appreciation for and why?

_____

_____

_____

_____

_____

_____

_____

I appreciate myself for how much I am choosing to enjoy my life more in the following ways:
At home, I am...

_____

_____

At work, I am...

_____

_____

With my friends, I am...

_____

_____

In my personal time, I am...

_____

_____

I am reaching for thoughts of appreciation about anything in my life that makes me feel fortunate to be who I am. I am living a life I love more every day. With my work or life in general, I feel *really* good about...

_____

_____

_____

_____

What I look forward to most about work is...

_____

_____

What I look forward to most about possible future work opportunities is...

_____

_____

I feel really good about myself because I am...

_____

_____

Every day I get better at letting go of...

_____

Every day I get better at...

_____

Who or what am I feeling especially thankful for and why?

_____

_____

_____

_____

If desired, send out wishes for more joy and wellbeing to them or anyone you will see in the next 24 hours.

Intentions for the Days Ahead

What's my intention for this coming week or so? What are all the words or phrases that describe it and how do I feel at the end of the week?

_____

_____

_____

_____

_____

_____

_____

Now, close your eyes and take about thirty seconds to visualize tomorrow and your week the way you want it to go from morning to night. See and feel the ease of it.

★ *First thing in the morning, ask:* "How do I wish to feel throughout my day today? I choose to feel _____."
What is inspiring me to be an example of peace and joy wherever I go?

For the next ten days, the topic will mainly be on what you wrote on Day 1 as your desired end result for…

My Personal Life is: _____. Please fill it in once again.

How much more can I nurture myself in a way that supports my wellbeing? The next ten days is primarily about gaining more personal freedom in how I think and feel and act. *Write a letter to your authentic self, stating what you desire for being more true to yourself. This could be about connecting to your spirituality or giving yourself the attention you deserve; doing more self-care, self-acceptance, self-advocacy, or being more lighthearted and fearless, or just honoring your own needs and desires in general.*

Dear Self,

_____

_____

_____

_____

_____

_____

_____

_____

_____

_____

_____

_____

_____

_____

_____

_____

_____

_____

_____

_____

_____

Why do I feel so free to be my authentic self now? I am now achieving more personal freedom. Yay! *Your turn:*
I am _____.

Intentions for My Day (Or tomorrow)

What words describe my day? I am feeling _____. I am being _____. I am having _____. I am doing _____. How will I look and feel at the end of the day? Imagine it now.

Day 72 _____

I'm getting really good at letting all my choices reflect my true preferences. And it feels so good to live this way. When I align with this energy, I feel free to express myself and do so as I please. I let myself be who I am and do what I love. I say yes when I mean yes, and no when I mean no. Showing my confidence in all my interactions comes naturally to me now, and my positive and peaceful energy is felt by all those around me. Could this be what it feels like when I allow myself to have more personal freedom? What is my life like when I've gotten to this point? Am I there now? This is how things feel to me when I'm there:

I am spending more time thinking about...

_____

Emotionally, I am feeling...

_____

Physically, I am feeling...

_____

I am feeling more confident about...

_____

I am feeling more connected to my true self because...

_____

I am being more authentic in my actions by...

_____

I am better every day at knowing what I truly want for myself and I am doing more of what I wish to do. I am...

_____

My life feels even better because I am...

_____

I am at ease with who I am and speak my truth straight from the heart. *Your turn*: I am _____.

✳ ✳ ✳ ✳ ✳ ✳ ✳ ✳ ✳ ✳ ✳ ✳

What do you love about your current personal life or level of freedom and why?

_____

_____

Intentions for My Day (Or tomorrow)

What words describe my day? I am feeling _____. I am being _____. I am having _____. I am doing _____. How will I look and feel at the end of the day? Imagine it now.

One of the first steps in achieving a higher level of wellbeing is feeling more deeply connected to myself. I become more aware of my true nature and what makes me happy and I find myself wanting to give myself more personal freedom to be and say and do what I choose. What does personal freedom mean to me?

_____

_____

How do I get there? Let's begin with where I'm at. What is going really well for me in this area? What have I been doing to support my personal needs and wants?

_____

_____

_____

When I'm not fulfilling necessary obligations to family or work, what am I spending my time doing for myself?

_____

_____

_____

In what ways do I love to spoil myself? What do I enjoy doing that is relaxing for me?

_____

_____

_____

What do I enjoy doing now that is fun for me? What has been making me smile or laugh more easily?

_____

_____

_____

What are my absolute favorite things to do of all time? Why do I enjoy it so much, and when can I do it again?

_____

_____

_____

What do people get to see in me? How much of myself am I showing them? Am I being true to myself, and letting my voice be heard? What comes out when I allow myself to fully relax and have fun or be real with people?

_____

_____

How easy is it to show them who I truly am versus what I want them to believe about me? Do I notice when I'm holding back? Do I ever find myself wishing I would have been more at ease, more talkative, or *less* talkative, and more confident, friendlier, or more straightforward than I was? I would rather be...

_____

How clearly or objectively am I able to view myself? Am I being fair to myself? Do I think of myself as confident, brave, and bold, or soft-spoken and timid? How do I wish to be? How do I see the real me? I am...

_____

_____

Write a description of how I think others see me when I'm showing my genuine self.

_____

_____

If I had a magic wand, what changes would I make in relation to having more personal freedom?

_____

_____

How would this change my life?

_____

_____

I believe it's achievable because...

_____

_____

If my intuition could speak to me about this, what would it tell me to do differently at home, work, or in my personal life, if anything? And what would it say more personal freedom will do for me?

_____

_____

_____

_____

More personal freedom is available to me. I am believing in my ability to have my life be how I want it to be, and more so every day. I am now achieving an atmosphere for success in allowing myself more personal freedom. *Your turn*: I am _____.

What do you love about what you're headed toward and why?

_____

_____

_____

Intentions for My Day (Or tomorrow)

What words describe my day? I am feeling _____. I am being _____. I am having _____. I am doing _____. How will I look and feel at the end of the day? Imagine it now.

I naturally align with more personal freedom when I practice being self-governed. I am confident in who I am and trust in my decision-making abilities. I think independently and live by my own rules without hesitation or self-deprivation. I trust my instincts and feel self-guided. If I want to practice feeling this way more often, I can decide how I want it to be, set some intentions, and keep guiding my thoughts there if any contradictory thoughts come up. With practice, this more consistent mindset comes naturally to me and soon I find myself being more confident than anyone I know. This is not about ego. It's about self-respect and an inner knowing that I know what's best for me.

How would I define my level of independent thinking?

_____

What are the daily or routine decisions that I make easily? Can I think of three or more?

_____

_____

How confident do I feel in my ability to make my decisions without consulting with someone first? Can I think of a couple that apply here? The kinds of decisions that I make easily at home, work, or in general are...

_____

_____

_____

I want to always respect my own opinions because...

_____

I want to stop second-guessing myself, if ever, and be more confident about...

_____

_____

_____

I want to stop seeking approval from others, if ever, and feel self-guided when making choices about...

_____

_____

How does it feel when I'm so self-assured in my own beliefs that I don't feel the need to defend my opinion to anyone? And to know that what is right for me is right for me, and their opinion is right for them? And be okay with all of it? What are the words that describe how free I feel when I fully value myself and don't need anyone to agree with me? I am now allowing myself to feel more confident about...

_____

_____

_____

How does it feel to know that *every* time I let go of a little more control, I'm doing wonders for my body and my wellbeing?

If or when I'm ready to, are there any boundaries I want to set for myself or others, other than the necessary family/work obligations?

_____

Is there anything I'm busying myself with that might not seem so important if I looked back on it five or ten years from now? Or is there anything I'm doing that I don't enjoy anymore? What am I saying no to now?

_____

Is there anything I could stop doing so I could spend more time with family or friends or work on a hobby or passion project of mine?

_____

When possible, and if desired, how do I feel about kindly and confidently letting others know that I sometimes have something I need to do for myself before I can help them?

_____

What activities do I enjoy doing for myself now, without hesitation, guilt, or offering excuses?

_____

I often tell myself that *I make the rules. I decide. I get to choose. I can do whatever I want.* And all the answers I seek are within me. I am free to be my most genuine self, the truest version of me that adores and supports me. I am owning up to this and making it mine.

If I imagined being led by the free-spirited side of me in every way, what might be different about my life?

_____

_____

_____

The more I align with my true nature, the more I set myself free from struggle. And the more I accept myself, the more I find myself accepting others. This can only bring me to a place of more ease, joy, and freedom. All resistance and self-doubt has left me, and I feel free. I am as free as I let myself be. *Your turn*: I am

_____.

What would the most loving, accepting part of me say about how I'm doing right now?
You are doing better every day in every way, even better than you think you are. You are...

_____

_____

_____

Intentions for My Day (Or tomorrow)

What words describe my day? I am feeling _____. I am being _____. I am having _____. I am doing _____. How will I look and feel at the end of the day? Imagine it now.
Let yourself have the kind of day that makes you feel free to live life your way!

This week is all about feeling free to live a life I love more every day. How comfortable and free do I feel to be myself in every area of my life? What part of my life feels the most comfortable and satisfying and why?

_____

_____

If I had it the way I wanted it, and felt the way I wanted to, I am free from...

_____

_____

I am free to...

_____

_____

I am fearless about...

_____

_____

If I were to go a little beyond my comfort zone, how fearlessly free do I want to be? How does it feel when I am completely trusting and fearlessly free in my mind? What are the words that would describe how I think that would feel?

_____

_____

When it's taken place and I'm in that state of mind, in what ways am I fearlessly bold and free in relation to: My work life...

_____

_____

My relationship or while on a date...

_____

_____

My personal life or with friends...

_____

_____

How free do I feel to freely say what I want and kindly do as I please with my partner, family or friends? What are some examples, real or desired?

_____

_____

How much more fearless or free can I feel right now and in the days and weeks ahead? When I'm feeling at ease with who I am, I am feeling...

_____

I am focused on...

_____

I feel aligned with...

_____

I might feel as if I'm breathing in the energy of...

_____

I allow myself to be...

_____

I allow myself to have...

_____

What I love most about having this come true is...

_____

How much more am I able to let this in right now? My mind is powerful and I have an incredible ability to take charge of how I feel. I love feeling my natural courage and invincibility.

When I am attuning to the harmony of my inner spirit, I am full of joy and feel free to be myself. As I confidently walk about my day, I do so with a slight smile on my face, with that little-known secret I cherish that all is well with *me*. I exude all of these qualities and never arrive anywhere without them. When I show up, there's no pretense whatsoever. I am so good at letting my authenticity show that I am virtually transparent. *Your turn*: I am _____. I love letting myself feel as free as I'm meant to feel!

What are you loving and appreciating about yourself or your day or life right now and why?

_____

_____

_____

_____

_____

Intentions for My Day (Or tomorrow)

What words describe my day? I am feeling _____. I am being _____. I am having _____. I am doing _____. How will I look and feel at the end of the day? Imagine it now.

Day 76 _____

How does it feel to give myself permission to do what I wish any time I want, when possible?

_____

In taking the next obvious step toward my goal, what actions can I take that I believe will help me achieve more personal freedom? What am I saying yes to? Can I see myself finding a way to do more of what I want for the sake of pure enjoyment? What are some new things you would like to try? Has anything been calling you?

If I had an unlimited amount of time to spend doing exactly what I wanted, and it wouldn't affect anyone else, what would I be doing? Where would I be going?

_____	_____	_____
_____	_____	_____
_____	_____	_____
_____	_____	_____
_____	_____	_____
_____	_____	_____
_____	_____	_____
_____	_____	_____
_____	_____	_____
_____	_____	_____
_____	_____	_____
_____	_____	_____
_____	_____	_____
_____	_____	_____
_____	_____	_____
_____	_____	_____
_____	_____	_____

What do you appreciate about this time you have to yourself? What do you love about it? How does it feel to be free to do anything you want, whenever you want, whether that is spending time alone or with your family or your partner or family or friends? Just let all the words of appreciation you feel for it flow onto the paper as quickly as you can, beginning with; I love my life. I love being me. I am so fortunate to be who I am. I love...

_____
_____
_____
_____
_____

_____

_____

_____

_____

_____

_____

_____

_____

_____

_____

_____

_____

_____

Close your eyes and imagine it being this way now. See yourself and how happy it makes you feel.

How much lighter and freer can I feel in my mind? How much lighter and freer can I feel in my body? How much more *lighthearted* am I able to feel right now? *Close your eyes and ask the questions again, and allow your body time to respond.* If I can feel this way more often, it will trickle into my life and bring more freedom and fun experiences for me. The more I practice guiding my thoughts like this, the more I'm able to transform my emotions to a better-feeling state any time I want.

Consider scheduling yourself for some "me time" weekly, biweekly, or monthly, and just go and do what pleases you. I'm in charge of making choices that make me feel happy and free, and I am committed to honoring my true feelings and allowing myself to have more fun. *Your turn*: I am

_____.

Which activity feels the most fun or satisfying to think about and why?
And which do you intend to do first and why?

_____

_____

_____

_____

_____

Intentions for My Day (Or tomorrow)

What words describe my day? I am feeling _____. I am being _____. I am having _____. I am doing _____. How will I look and feel at the end of the day? Imagine it now.

It's time to practice my belief and expectation of things working out for me. So how do I see myself as who I am now becoming? What do I envision in terms of my overall wellbeing, as well as a sense of personal freedom?

_____
_____
_____
_____
_____
_____

What do I envision in terms of my success in finding even more joy in life?

_____
_____
_____
_____
_____

How am I letting myself shine in every area of my life?

_____
_____
_____
_____

I love feeling focused and unstoppable in my spirit of joy and freedom! I trust that so many things are working out for me. What do I believe is on its way to me?

_____
_____
_____
_____

I feel free to think about...

_____
_____
_____

I feel free to be...

_____
_____

I feel free to have…

_____

_____

_____

I feel free to do…

_____

_____

_____

I am starting to feel more fearless about…

_____

_____

_____

I expect things to continue feeling better every day in every way because…

_____

_____

I completely embrace who I am now and who I'm becoming. It just keeps getting better! I am feeling so liberated, and feel free to live my life more authentically. I'm doing what I wish and saying what I choose, and it's all feeling so natural to me now. Confident, easy, and free. I trust that I am on my path to more personal freedom and way more fun. *Your turn*: I am _____.

How much more are you able to believe in your ability to achieve such a tremendous sense of wellbeing and fearlessness that you're feeling safe, confident, and able to be yourself no matter where you are or who you're with?
And what part of your desired outcome do you believe in most and why?

_____

_____

_____

_____

_____

_____

Intentions for My Day (Or tomorrow)

What words describe my day? I am feeling _____. I am being _____. I am having _____. I am doing _____. How will I look and feel at the end of the day? Imagine it now.

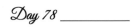

I focus on positive solutions, and it sets me free. Is there anything going on currently that I wish to find a solution for? If desired, think of a recent situation with an individual or group, or just something that's weighing on the mind. How do I want things to be? What would I rather have happen if I could replay the scene or have it turn out that way the next time it occurs, if applicable?

_____

_____

_____

_____

_____

_____

Additionally, what's another way to look at this situation that makes me feel better about it?

_____

_____

_____

_____

_____

Is there anything I can do that will make things easier?

_____

_____

_____

_____

_____

How would it feel to have this situation be really comfortable for me?

_____

_____

_____

What are the words to describe how I feel when a better outcome is taking place?

_____

_____

_____

What are the words to describe how I feel afterward, as well as how I feel when I notice that things are continuing to get better and easier for everyone involved?

_____

_____

_____

I can close my eyes right now and see my desired end result. I see everyone involved doing better and feel that it's all that I hoped it would be, or better.

On another note, whenever I have a fear-based or self-doubting thought, I practice a habit of redirecting it with an affirmation like: "Everything always works out for me." It may sound simple, but it's a very powerful statement that can change my life in the best possible way, once that frequent thought becomes a belief.

If there's ever any stressful moments, I remember to think, "I choose wellbeing" to remind me that feeling good and allowing my mind and body to be at ease is more important than anything to me, and vital to supporting my desire for total wellbeing. I am now allowing myself to feel more amused by anything that used to annoy me. I am better every day at guiding myself to align with more happiness and freedom. *Your turn*: I am

_____.

What do you love about your current state of mind around your self-worth and why?
*And what do you love about feeling completely comfortable being your true self
with anyone and everyone, and why?*

_____
_____
_____
_____
_____
_____
_____
_____
_____
_____
_____
_____
_____
_____
_____
_____
_____
_____
_____
_____

Intentions for My Day (Or tomorrow)

What words describe my day? I am feeling _____. I am being _____. I am having _____. I am doing _____. How will I look and feel at the end of the day? Imagine it now.

I am free by nature and I have the gift of free will. I like believing it's always okay to do everything my way. And I'm doing it all in a *great* way! A way that feels good and is just right for *me*. As if I'm holding my own debut or an unveiling, I am letting myself shine in every area of my life. Who have I become and what do I intend for my future? Here's a list of ways that I'm letting myself shine and feel self-governed, self-accepting, empowered, or what I love about my personal choices and my ability to have the freedom I desire. Let it flow freely, categorize it as above, or use A-Z, as desired.

_____   _____   _____
_____   _____   _____
_____   _____   _____
_____   _____   _____
_____   _____   _____
_____   _____   _____
_____   _____   _____
_____   _____   _____
_____   _____   _____
_____   _____   _____
_____   _____   _____
_____   _____   _____
_____   _____   _____
_____   _____   _____
_____   _____   _____

How does it feel when I allow myself to breathe in the energy of freedom and joy? Body, show me how it feels. Breathing in and out, I put my attention on my heart center and feel it getting lighter and freer. How much more am I able to feel this way now and in the days ahead? Why is it suddenly so easy for me to start feeling this way, and more so every day? I am in the qualities and energy of joy and freedom.

If desired, 1) Make note of anything you practiced in the past ten days that felt good to you and you wish to continue. 2) Add your favorite thought-provoking question and affirmation to the list you started.

I am now achieving a sense of personal freedom that is supporting my total wellbeing. *Your turn*: I am

_____.

Intentions for My Day (Or tomorrow)

What words describe my day? I am feeling _____. I am being _____. I am having _____. I am doing _____. How will I look and feel at the end of the day? Imagine it now.

Day 80 _____

More Appreciation & Intentions

My love for myself and appreciation for all that's in my life is bringing out the best in me. I know that I am more successful in all areas of my life because of it. And I like believing that love and acceptance brings out the best in everyone.

What was my favorite part about today or this past week?

_____

_____

What are three or more things I felt appreciation for and why?

_____

_____

_____

_____

I love it when I reach that state of mind where everything feels easier and more satisfying to me. What do I feel satisfied about when I think of:

My family: _____

My home and its location: _____

My friends: _____

My personal life: _____

My workplace and the work I do: _____

If any, which areas feel like they're getting better in some way?

_____

Allow yourself to feel deep satisfaction with any part of your life that feels great to you, and the rest will come along. It will be your practiced thought until you find yourself in a new and better experience, if desired. *Whatever is meant to be will be. Life is good and I am free.*

In what ways has my life been feeling easier for me? Life in general is easier because...

_____

_____

_____

My home or family life is easier because...

_____

_____

_____

My work life is easier because...

_____

_____

_____

My relationship is easier because...

_____

_____

_____

My daily routine is easier because...

_____

_____

_____

How much easier has it become for me to meet new people and have a comfortable conversation with them?

_____

_____

_____

If I could have one more area of my life be easier for me, what would I choose? How do I want things to be?

_____

_____

_____

What can I do to initiate that change? What would be the obvious next step to take when I'm ready?

_____

Intentions for the Days Ahead

What's my intention for this coming week or so? What are all the words or phrases that describe it and how do I feel at the end of the week?

_____

_____

_____

_____

_____

Now, close your eyes and take about thirty seconds to visualize tomorrow and your week the way you want it to go from morning to night. See and feel the freedom in it.

   ★ *First thing in the morning, ask:* "How do I wish to feel throughout my day today? I choose to feel _____."
What is inspiring me to feel free to be myself?

A WISH Moment for Inspiration
Words Inspire Spiritual Harmony

This is Day 18, a chapter from *100 Days of Actions & Intentions to Create the Life You Wish For*. It seemed like a good time to include this.

Day 18

Wellbeing Is a Part of Who I Am

Whenever I start a sentence with "I am now," or "I decided," it means to me that in that moment of that decision or statement, a change is occurring. An energy shift is evident. And the words that follow that phrase are in the process of happening the moment it's spoken.

It's a commitment and intention to do something. It means I know I can do it. And I *will* do it. And in that moment or minutes, hours, days, or in some cases months to follow, it is *all* happening.

I love my powerful words, thoughts, and intentions. And I *love* using them to the best of my ability to create the positive transformation I *know* is inevitable for me.

I love knowing that *I decided that blissful wellbeing is a part of me*. It's who I am. It's all I know. I released any beliefs that didn't serve me, and I continue to practice the feeling state of blissful wellbeing. It's become all I know. Nothing else enters my mind.

How did I get here?

I made my powerful intentions known.
And I decided to be in charge of how I feel.
I am now allowing my body the ease it requires to let my wellbeing flow freely.
I continue making peace with worries and fears or anything I consider a problem.
I am frequently guiding my thoughts to a blissful place.
I am staying open to positive change.
I am now being more mindfully present in the joy of the moment.
And I am letting my emotions guide me and making choices that feel right to me.
I started purposely living a life I love.

I decided to practice being in a state of complete wellbeing until it felt like a part of me. And it's now become a part of who I am. I knew it was simply a choice I could make. And instead of looking for things that could be *wrong*, I started noticing and appreciating what was going *right* for me.

I am now creating new thought patterns that are programming new beliefs.
And new neural pathways are being built in response to my new beliefs.
And they're being strengthened with repetition of my happy thoughts.

So I am now activating my highest vibration to create the highest level of wellbeing for me.

It's so great to know that my higher energies will always override any lower energies I have. So while I frequently stay focused in a good-feeling place, my body and everything in my life is transforming to accommodate my wishes.

I am now designing a life I love more every day. The one I'm meant to be living. Things always work out for me, and everything is falling into place. As I hold my vision of blissful wellbeing, I am now allowing for a remarkable transformation to take place anywhere it's needed or desired.

How does it feel when I am living a life of blissful wellbeing?

How do I answer the following questions *from the mindset of total and blissful wellbeing*? Think of one or more answers to each question.

> How do I feel?
> Do I feel a sense of relief or freedom?
> Why does it feel so easy for me now to achieve or maintain a healthier body and a happier state of mind?
> How does it feel now that I've achieved it?
> What does feeling good mean to me now?
> What does being happy mean to me now?
> When did I start seeing that all things are possible for me?
> How am I letting it change my life?
> How has it changed my family life?
> How has it changed my work life?
> How has it changed my personal life?
> What am I doing that I wasn't doing before?

I am now choosing to *always* feel the way I was intended to feel when I came into this world. I hold a vision of myself in the state I wish to be in. It's a part of me now. I live it and breathe it.

And the results of my positive thoughts are being shown to me by the way my body feels, and the way that I *easily* and *freely* move through life. It's as though my path has been cleared or laid out for me and all I have to do is simply *allow* good things to happen for me.

Every day in every way I am *more*. More aligned with blissful wellbeing. More aligned with my true nature. More passionate. More loving. More energetic. More courageous. More at peace. And more connected and in tune with who I am.

And every day in every way I'm better at allowing myself to be in the lighthearted energy I know is my true authentic self.

Action: Imagine it's three to six months from now and you've achieved your desire for an even higher level of wellbeing. You love and appreciate where you are now, but it's become even better. You've taken the time to go within and connect with your energy and inner guidance. Decisions have become easier. Life has become easier and more fun for you in every possible way. Let's say that you've achieved *all* your desires for your body, your energy, your clarity, and your life, as you imagined them to be or better. Imagine it's ten times better. Or a hundred times better!

Now, close your eyes and see an image of yourself walking toward you as you envision yourself. What do you see? Can you imagine yourself in a state of blissful wellbeing with a smile on your face? You're feeling *really* good. You're confident. You're feeling at ease and on *top* of the world.

The energy in and around your head feels *lighter* and *freer*. The energy in and around your *entire* body feels lighter and freer. There's no tension. There's no struggle. There's nothing cluttering your mind. And you're *completely* free to do anything you desire.

Take your time and visualize yourself in this state while you're at home, work, or socializing, traveling, or doing anything you'd love to be doing. Do what you can to feel the sensation of being there; see it, feel it, taste it, and touch it.

As the image gets closer and closer, the last thing you notice is your face glowing in the sunlight right before this energy becomes part of you. It *is* you. It's already done. It's yours to align with and available to you now. Close your eyes and take yourself there now.

Hold this vision in your mind. Daydream of it often or as you drift off to sleep. If you have trouble visualizing it, think of your favorite photo of yourself, or write out the details of your vision now or before you go to sleep.

Use the space below for this or use a separate piece of paper so you can leave it by your bed and read it before you go to sleep each night, if desired. Remember, it's just the feeling of joy and wellbeing you're trying to evoke, which can bring more of it to you. Allow yourself to feel excited about what's to come!

_____

_____

_____

_____

_____

_____

_____

_____

_____

_____

_____

_____

_____

_____

_____

_____

_____

_____

_____

_____

_____

_____

_____

_____

_____

_____

★ I Am More Aligned With Blissful Wellbeing Every Day

For the next ten days, the topic will mainly be on what you wrote on Day 1 as your desired end result for...

My Dreams and Plans are: _____. Please fill it in once again. You are allowing your wishes and dreams to be a part of who you are. The more it feels that way, the more it becomes so, and the sooner they become yours. It's important to dream. It inspires us and gives us something to look forward to. So, imagine you're having a conversation with your biggest dream or highest priority, or a symbol that represents *all* your wishes and dreams. Tell it what you want, why you want it, what it will do for you when you have it, and how it will change your life.

Dear Wishes and Dreams,

_____

_____

_____

_____

_____

_____

_____

_____

_____

_____

_____

_____

_____

_____

_____

_____

_____

_____

_____

_____

_____

I am now achieving all my wishes and dreams. *Your turn*: I am _____.

Intentions for My Day (Or tomorrow)

What words describe my day? I am feeling _____. I am being _____. I am having _____. I am doing _____. How will I look and feel at the end of the day? Imagine it now.

Here are some questions to get me thinking about what I want my ideal life to be like...

What are my wishes and dreams? What are my goals or deepest desires? What's becoming most important to me? What is calling me? What keeps coming to mind that might just be my life purpose or a hint of a new passion that's waiting for me to discover it?

_____

_____

_____

_____

_____

What would I love to do for work? What hobby would I love to be doing full-time and get paid really well for it? Is there something I'm really good at that would bring value to others?

_____

_____

Not that I need to, but what courses would I take or what new things would I love to learn? Or what would I like to teach?

_____

_____

_____

What would I *love* my future to be like for me?

_____

_____

What would my perfect day be like?

_____

_____

In what ways would I like to spoil myself?

_____

_____

_____

What would I love to do with my family?

_____

_____

_____

Where do I want to travel to? Who would I go with?

_____

What material things do I wish for?

_____

_____

_____

What gifts would I give myself? What gifts would I like to give to others?

_____

_____

_____

_____

_____

What qualities do I want to make my own, and how do I want to feel?

_____

_____

What is one thing I *really, really* want more than anything?

_____

Is there anything in my life I wish to change or improve upon?

_____

_____

Is there anything I'm still doing that I don't enjoy anymore?

_____

When I'm ready, I intend to trade it in for something that lights me up!

I am now aligning with the energy of all my wishes and dreams. *Your turn*: I am

_____.

What do you love about your life right now and why?

_____

_____

_____

_____

_____

Intentions for My Day (Or tomorrow)

What words describe my day? I am feeling _____. I am being _____. I am having _____. I am doing _____. How will I look and feel at the end of the day? Imagine it now.

I am now achieving an atmosphere for success in achieving all my wishes and dreams. How do I want to feel about my wishes and dreams? How much do I believe in them?

_____

_____

_____

How much do I believe in myself and my ability to achieve them? How achievable do they feel to me? I believe in my ability to achieve my goals and dreams because...

_____

_____

_____

_____

_____

_____

_____

What are the many reasons I am worthy of all my wishes and dreams? What if I could strip away anything that ever made me think that I wasn't enough? What if I could feel as worthy as I truly deserve to feel? Could there *be* any valid question about my worthiness to be happy or achieve my goals? No, never! I deserve all my dreams to come true because...

_____

_____

_____

_____

_____

_____

_____

_____

_____

_____

_____

_____

_____

_____

_____

The reason I want this to happen is...

_____
_____
_____

If I had a magic wand, what three wishes would I make right now?

_____
_____
_____

How would this change my life?

_____
_____
_____
_____

What state of mind do I think I need to be in to achieve it? What are some new thoughts I could practice to align with the energy of my desires?

_____
_____
_____
_____
_____
_____
_____

The more worthy and abundant I feel, the closer I am to *all* my desires. I am also keeping in mind that there is a vibrational version of every desire I have and they want me as much as I want them. Our energies are aligning and I am ready! *Your turn*: I am _____.

What do you love about what's to come and why?

_____
_____
_____

Intentions for My Day (Or tomorrow)

What words describe my day? I am feeling _____. I am being _____. I am having _____. I am doing _____. How will I look and feel at the end of the day? Imagine it now.

If my wishes and dreams could speak to me, what do I think they would say? They're telling me what they will do for me, how they will improve my life, and what they want me to do to achieve them. Make a list of goals or dreams on the left and leave space between each one to write the answers.

_____

_____

_____

_____

_____

_____

_____

_____

_____

_____

_____

_____

_____

_____

_____

_____

_____

_____

_____

_____

_____

_____

_____

_____

_____

_____

_____

_____

_____

_____

_____

_____

_____

_____

_____

_____

_____

_____

_____

_____

_____

_____

_____

_____

_____

_____

_____

_____

_____

Now look at each desire on your list, one at a time, and close your eyes to picture it. See it in front of you and imagine you're breathing in the energy of it. In your second breath, see yourself moving toward it or watch it coming toward you. Then feel that you're experiencing it in some way, whether you're touching it, walking inside, using it, or showing it to someone. Do your best to feel the emotion associated with being there. Let a smile form on your face. Imagine this often if it feels good.

My life is now transforming to accommodate my every wish. I am keeping these images impressed upon my mind. I am becoming one with the energy of my desires and making them mine. *Your turn*: I am

_____.

How are you feeling today and why do you think that is?
If you think you could feel even better, what are the words that would describe it?
Breathe in the meaning of each word as it's written.

_____

_____

_____

_____

_____

_____

_____

Intentions for My Day (Or tomorrow)

What words describe my day? I am feeling _____. I am being _____. I am having _____. I am doing _____. How will I look and feel at the end of the day? Imagine it now.

Where my attention goes, energy flows, and that's why my desires are taking form and finding their way toward me. Our energies are linking up in some kind of synchronistic dance. How does it feel to walk into a day in my ideal life as I wish it to be?

Describe what it's like to be, have, and do exactly what you envision for yourself, or better. Take yourself through one area of your life at a time and describe what it looks and feels like. For example, imagine you're waking up in your cozy bed in your new house, and later at the desk of your new office, or perhaps you're on vacation with your family. Describe how your day unfolds in each place, as though you're walking yourself through every activity. Give lots of details on what you're doing, what you can reach out and touch in each place, what you love about it, and what you love about how it feels to be there.

_____

_____

_____

_____

_____

_____

_____

_____

_____

_____

_____

_____

_____

_____

_____

_____

_____

_____

_____

_____

_____

_____

_____

_____

_____

_____

_____

_____
_____
_____
_____
_____
_____
_____
_____
_____
_____
_____
_____
_____
_____

Now close your eyes and imagine how it feels to be living it. My life circumstances are now transforming to accommodate my every wish. I am keeping the image of all my wishes and dreams impressed upon my mind. I am becoming one with the energy of limitless abundance and making them mine.

How much more abundant am I able to feel in the days and weeks ahead? I am now achieving the feeling of limitless abundance and attracting all good things to me. *Your turn*: I am _____.
Why is it becoming so easy for me to own the power that allows me to create the life I wish for?

What are the many things you are loving and appreciating about your life right now and why?

_____
_____
_____
_____
_____
_____
_____
_____
_____

Intentions for My Day (Or tomorrow)

What words describe my day? I am feeling _____. I am being _____. I am having _____. I am doing _____. How will I look and feel at the end of the day? Imagine it now.

Write a list of all the things you want to see happen for you 1) this coming year, 2) within 3-5 years, 3) in your lifetime. Include any milestones you'd like to reach for your overall wellbeing, goals, projects, wishes, or dreams, and be sure to include some of life's little pleasures. I am now achieving...

Within a Year	Within 3-5 Years	In My Lifetime

Now circle those that feel the most satisfying or exciting to think about.

Do I feel inspired to act on any of them *now*? Am I allowing myself time for quiet moments that let in the ideas that my inner guidance is always sending me, and I may notice by way of good-feeling impulses, such as; to make a call, go somewhere, or look something up? What do I imagine it would tell me to focus on or do first? What feels best?

_____

_____

_____

Out of those you circled, pick one or more out of those that feel the most achievable to you. One at a time break them down into smaller steps by asking what action feels like the obvious next step to reach that goal. And the next and the next until you have a list of steps from where you are to where you want to be.

_____

_____

_____

_____
_____
_____
_____
_____
_____
_____
_____
_____
_____
_____
_____

If any of your goals do not yet feel achievable or you can't think of the obvious next step, you can take a few minutes on occasion or when desired to research the topic. Such as watching a video about how to do something you're wanting to achieve. This can help to build confidence and give you ideas or clarification on any subject.

But know that all the answers are within you and the path to get to where you want to be is unfolding naturally and easily when you let it be that way for you. And for anything you do in life, your way is the best way.

How much more inspired can I feel? How many more brilliant ideas can come to me with effortless ease? How much more action can I be inspired to take? How much more determination can I feel for getting started on a project I'm wanting to do? How much more excited can I get about this now or in the days ahead? Do your best to only take action steps when you're feeling inspired to. Sometimes it's when you stop trying, or realize you don't have to do any searching for your desire and just let it come to you, that it shows up.

Consider buying a notebook or journal that is for the sole purpose of writing out goals and dreams and breaking them down into small steps. Then do your best to wait for the inspiration to act on taking the obvious next step toward meeting that goal. _I am feeling more inspired every day to take the next step toward my goal. Your turn_: I am _____.

✱ ·٠• ·٠• ·٠• ✱ ·٠• ✱ ·٠• ·٠• ✱ ·٠• ·٠• ✱ ·٠•

Which goal is your favorite and why?
And what do you believe is the first step you will take toward your goal and why?

_____
_____
_____
_____

Intentions for My Day (Or tomorrow)

What words describe my day? I am feeling _____. I am being _____. I am having _____. I am doing _____. How will I look and feel at the end of the day? Imagine it now.

It's time to practice my belief and expectation of my goals, wishes, and dreams working out for me. Why am I feeling so certain that everything in my life is becoming better every day in every way? I am always in the right place at the right time and moving toward a better place. How much more trusting am I able to feel about everything working out for me? How does it feel when I allow myself to receive limitless abundance?

In relation to my life and what I expect to happen for me, what does limitless abundance mean to me and what areas of my life do I see or feel abundance flowing now? In what areas do I expect it to come into?

_____

_____

What if I knew that feeling more appreciation for the abundance I see around me would create more of it in all forms? What signs of abundance have I been noticing recently? Things like nature, kindness, happy couples, successful people, and meeting like-minded people or hearing laughter and pleasant conversations.

_____

_____

What if I could circulate more wealth in my life by staying open to giving and receiving gifts of caring, affection, compliments, appreciation, or things? How much more receptive can I be? What gifts or compliments have I received in the past and what did I appreciate about that?

_____

_____

_____

What gifts or compliments have I given out recently that were from the heart, rather than obligation? What made me do it and what felt good about it? If nothing comes to mind, what have I thought about doing?

_____

_____

What if I could offer gifts in the form of wishes for prosperity and knew that it would help keep the abundance flowing in my life and in the world? What wishes do I feel inspired to give out right now?

_____

_____

_____

When I can believe in my success and genuinely feel happy for the success of others, I know that I am aligning with my natural state of abundance, and all forms of wealth can flow more easily. How happy do I feel for those I see living abundantly or who have something I want? Can I think of anyone in particular that I am happy for and why?

_____

_____

_____

I am abundant in nature and the better I feel, the more abundance will flow. It can also help to increase my wealth consciousness and get more comfortable with receiving abundance in all forms, including money. It's just another form of energy so there's no limit to it, and it's available to all. To be more receptive to it, I notice that:

> Money has always been flowing in my life, and it's going to continue flowing into my life. It's increasing in volume as I embrace the idea of money without any thought of the lack of it. The thought of not enough money never enters my mind. There will always be more than enough. The more I spend, the more I make. The more at ease I am with spending, and the more I enjoy what I buy with it, the more easily it flows to me. And it's nice to know the more I wish prosperity for others, the more I attract to me. It's showing itself to me. My life is going my way. And my way is always just right for me. What I seek is seeking me, and all the answers are within me.

The more I practice these thoughts, the more I notice it's true. But, it's not about money, is it? It's really about having the freedom to do more of what I love to do, and how good that feels. That being said, here are some fun questions to get me thinking about what I would love to be, have, or do without limitation. So let's begin...

If I had an extra $100 dollars a day and I had to spend it before the end of the day, what would I spend it on?

_____

If I had an extra $100,000 dollars right now and had to spend it within three months, what would I spend it on?

_____

_____

If I had an extra $1,000,000 dollars and had to spend it within three years, what would I spend it on?

_____

_____

_____

_____

If I had another million dollars every three years after that, what would I be spending it on?

_____

_____

_____

_____

It can show up in various forms from various sources. It can also be a priceless amount of joy that is equivalent to that amount of money. It's up to me. How much more abundant am I able to feel right now and in the days and weeks ahead? I am a magnet for all my life's wishes. I am as aligned with my wishes and dreams as I believe I am. I move forward with faith and purpose and expect them to manifest, as I imagine them, or better. *Your turn*: I am _____.

Intentions for My Day (Or tomorrow)

What words describe my day? I am feeling _____. I am being _____. I am having _____. I am doing _____. How will I look and feel at the end of the day? Imagine it now.

Day 88 _____

Today is a day for solutions. To help my wishes and dreams along, I want to feel receptive to them and line up with their energy. To do so, I need to let go of any limiting beliefs and feel worthy of my desires. I need to believe in my dreams and expect them to come true, and stay open to whatever way that happens. And for the best possible results, I need to practice a frequent state of joy and appreciation. This allows me to align with *all* my desires more easily.

How does it feel to be completely receptive to anything I wish for? So much so, that I become magnetic to all that I love, all that I want, and all that I deserve? If I can focus on one or more things in my life that make me feel really happy, I will hold an active vibration that aligns me with *all* my desires, and I will start seeing results. What are some things that bring me the most joy that I can think of or do more often?

_____
_____
_____
_____
_____

On a scale from 1-10, how much do I value myself or my ability to achieve anything I set out to do?

_____

How magnetic do I feel to my desires and what do I believe I'm attracting right now? I can tell by what's showing up for me each day. I am attracting...

_____
_____
_____
_____
_____
_____
_____
_____

Briefly think of any self-doubting or limiting thoughts that come to mind often or on occasion, if any. For each one, ask: What ever made me think this in the first place? Whose belief is this; mine or someone else's? Could it possibly be true?

_____
_____
_____
_____
_____
_____
_____

What is the most convincing speech I could give myself that would help me eliminate these thoughts? What are the many reasons they are completely untrue? What would I tell a friend with the same concerns?

_____

_____

_____

_____

_____

_____

_____

Then come up with some affirmation statements that mean the complete opposite.

_____

_____

_____

_____

_____

_____

_____

How much more magnetic to my desires can I be today and in all the days to come? How much more magnetic can I be to ideal opportunities for me? There's nothing in the way of what I want. Living abundantly can come easily for me if I let it. I am abundant by nature. It's just a matter of practicing the way I *truly* want to feel more of the time. I am not needing to clear blocks to abundance or anything else. I am just tuning in to what I want and the rest falls away as I take my attention off of it. Total wellbeing is my natural state.

I am now putting my energy into all the great things I *want* to experience. And this is how I *always* get to where I want to be. If something doesn't work out, I trust that it's leaving me open for something *even* better to come.

I can get myself to a place where I have a one-pointed focus on aligning with the harmony of my true nature and all good things must come. I am the master of my mind. I am the master of my day. And the master of my life. *Your turn*: I am _____.

***. . . . . . *** . . . . *** . . . . . . *** . . . . *** . . . . . . *** . . . . *** . . . . . . *** . . . .

What do you love about your current mindset around money/wealth or abundance being limitless and why?

_____

_____

_____

_____

Intentions for My Day (Or tomorrow)

What words describe my day? I am feeling _____. I am being _____. I am having _____. I am doing _____. How will I look and feel at the end of the day? Imagine it now.

I am practicing how it feels to be in the qualities and energy that will attract my wishes and dreams. Basically, I follow my heart's desire and do what I believe will bring me more joy and abundance. If I can imagine that every consistent thought I have is like a magnet for my wishes and dreams and I was getting back exactly what I was giving out, what would I choose to think about? How would I be acting? What would I choose to do with my time? *Write a list of words or phrases that answer these questions.*

I am thinking about...	I am acting like...	I am spending my time...

I am aligning with my ideal future as I practice an abundance mindset. Love has a high frequency and is my greatest power for attracting more joy, wellbeing, and abundance. When I feel that I am in a state of love for anything I desire, I line up with its energy. It becomes a part of me and must become my reality. Think of it as being in the same space, place, or energy of love, rather than "in-love," as in adoration. Or it can be both, of course.

When I have an abundance mindset, I feel in *love* with every joyful part of my life. I am in *love* with...

_____

_____

_____

_____

_____

I am in *love* with who I am because...

_____

_____

_____

_____

_____

I am in *love* with my mind because...

_____

_____

I am in *love* with my perfectly functioning body because...

_____

_____

I am in *love* with how I live my life because...

_____

_____

_____

_____

I am in *love* with how I feel because...

_____

_____

I am in *love* with the simple things like...

_____

_____

_____

_____

I am in *love* with my desires because...

_____

_____

_____

_____

I am in *love* with love because...

_____

_____

_____

I am also appreciating any contrast that comes up for helping me know what I don't want and strengthening my desire for an easier, better life. I am appreciating the opportunities it has given me for more personal growth, such as...

_____

_____

_____

I am in *love* with my endless abilities because...

_____

_____

_____

Why do I think my life is getting better every day? What areas of my life are getting better? And why is that?

_____

_____

_____

_____

_____

To the best of my ability, I am practicing how it feels to be one with this energy. I am living and breathing it. It's all happening now or in the days, weeks, or months to come, with effortless ease. Perhaps I'm there already!

If desired, 1) Make note of anything you practiced in the past ten days that felt good to you and you wish to continue. 2) Add your favorite thought-provoking question and affirmation to the list you started.

I am now achieving a sense of fearless freedom, harmony, and limitless abundance that supports my dreams and blissful wellbeing. *Your turn*: I am _____.

You've just met someone new and they'd like to know more about you.
You're telling them all about who you are and what your life is like upon achieving your dreams.
What would you tell them and what is their response? What questions are they asking you?

_____

_____

_____

_____

_____

_____

_____

_____

_____

_____

Intentions for My Day (Or tomorrow)

What words describe my day? I am feeling _____. I am being _____. I am having _____. I am doing _____. How will I look and feel at the end of the day? Imagine it now. Whenever I see something I want, I say, "Anything is possible." I don't have to search for it. *It's* coming to me.

Day 90 _____

More Appreciation & Intentions

What was my favorite part about today or this past week?

_____

What are three or more things I felt appreciation for and why?

_____
_____
_____
_____
_____

What are some things that happened or that I did that made me feel more abundant or connected to my desires?

_____
_____
_____

I appreciate myself for deciding to take inspired action toward my goals, now or in the weeks/months to come, in the following ways:
At home, I am...

_____
_____
_____

At work, I am...

_____
_____
_____

In my personal time, I am...

_____
_____
_____

What do I love and appreciate about my goals and dreams?

_____
_____
_____
_____

I feel really good about myself right now because I am...

_____

_____

Who or what am I feeling especially thankful for and why?

_____

If desired, send out wishes for more joy and wellbeing to them or anyone you will see in the next 24 hours.

Intentions for the Days Ahead

What are all the words or phrases that describe what I expect my life to feel like in the weeks or months to come?

_____

_____

_____

_____

_____

_____

_____

Whatever I consistently think of, believe, and expect has the power to attract anything I want. So I like to hold a vision or a symbol in mind that represents all my wishes and dreams. What does it look like? If I had a photograph, painting, or vision board of everything I wanted, what would be in it?

_____

_____

_____

_____

_____

_____

_____

How does it feel when I allow myself to feel magnetic to my desires? I could ask myself this question daily to remind me that I am able to align with my heart's desire. I can be anything. I can have anything. I can do anything!

With every breath I take, I am more and more attuned to the harmony, fearless freedom, and limitless abundance of my inner being. By nature, I am in a state of blissful wellbeing and it's time for me to feel good all day, *every* day. And that's what I intend to do. I deserve to feel good.

★ *First thing in the morning, ask:* "How do I wish to feel throughout my day today? I choose to feel _____."

These last ten days will be on a review of previous topics, as well as what you wrote on Day 1 as your desired end result for...

My Ideal Future is: _____. Please fill it in once again. Write a letter to (or from) your future self, about 6 months from now, telling a detailed story of who you've become. Explain how good you're feeling about yourself, your life, or anything you wish, and why you appreciate it so much. Again, this may feel strange, but it will help you energetically connect with your desired outcome. Think of it like an invitation to bring this into your life, and you're just getting ready for it. As your energy aligns with it, it will begin to unfold and reveal itself. Bit by bit, piece by piece, or perhaps all at once. As you hoped, or even better!

Dear Future Self,

_____

_____

_____

_____

_____

_____

_____

_____

_____

_____

_____

_____

_____

_____

_____

_____

_____

_____

_____

How does it feel when I am in the energy that allows all of my desires to manifest? Each little piece is coming my way and falling into place, all in perfect timing. *Your turn*: I am _____.

Intentions for My Day (Or tomorrow)

What words describe my day? I am feeling _____. I am being _____. I am having _____. I am doing _____. How will I look and feel at the end of the day? Imagine it now.

Do you remember these questions from day one?

So how do I want my life to go?
Where am I now, and where do I want to be?
Do I wish to make any changes?

Take a moment to check in and notice if any of your desires have changed or expanded in any way since day one. Fill in the fields below once again to reflect your current desires or desired end result.

A Wish List for Improving My Overall Wellbeing

My Health is: _____

My Mind is: _____

My Body looks and feels: _____

I Am Feeling: _____

My Home and Family are: _____

My Relationship is: _____

My Work Life is: _____

My Personal Life is: _____

My Dreams and Plans are: _____

My Ideal Future is: _____

Once again, describe in detail how it feels to be living your ideal future in all areas of your life. How would you be feeling? What would you be doing or where would you be going? Who would you be with? What would you be talking about? Dream big and fill in all the details.

Home Life:

_____
_____
_____
_____
_____
_____

Relationship/Dating or Single Life:

_____
_____
_____
_____
_____
_____
_____

Work Life:

_____
_____
_____
_____
_____
_____

Social/ Personal Life:

_____
_____
_____
_____
_____
_____

How does it *feel* to be living it? *Once again, close your eyes and imagine it now.* If I can believe it, I can achieve it, and my intelligent mind will find ways to bring it to me. Especially when I know and feel that I already have it. I am feeling abundant and open and receptive to more of it. There's no limit to the amount of joy and abundance I can have. It just keeps getting better.

In order to effortlessly align with this, my only work is to be in the joy of who I am as often as I can. I am just following my heart's desire by choosing what feels good to me. I am now aligning with the energy of my blissful wellbeing. *Your turn*: I am _____.

★ I am now achieving a state of blissful wellbeing. How does it feel when I allow myself to feel blissful? *Reminder: If it feels good, your homework is to ask yourself this question as often as you'd like.*

What part of your ideal future feels the most satisfying to think about and why?

_____
_____
_____
_____
_____
_____

Intentions for My Day (Or tomorrow)

What words describe my day? I am feeling _____. I am being _____. I am having _____. I am doing _____. How will I look and feel at the end of the day? Imagine it now.

I am speaking to the ease of achieving my goals. I love when it feels easy to allow my wishes and dreams to flow. I am letting them come to me. There's nothing I need to do but follow my heart or anything I feel guided to do. I am thankful for all of it coming to me so easily because...

_____

_____

I love when it feels easy to feel good because...

_____

_____

_____

_____

I love when it feels easy to have clarity because...

_____

_____

_____

_____

I love when it feels easy to be energetic because...

_____

_____

_____

_____

I love when it feels easy to make progress on my goals because...

_____

_____

_____

_____

I love when it feels easy to have all of my wants and needs because...

_____

_____

_____

_____

I love when it starts being easy for me to feel truly blissful more of the time because...

_____

_____

_____

If my intuition could tell me how to easily align with my ideal future, what do I think it would tell me? What thoughts and emotions would it encourage me to have? What would it tell me to spend my time and energy on?

_____

_____

_____

_____

_____

_____

_____

_____

_____

If desired, start writing anything that comes to mind that you wish to achieve in a new journal that you can call your "Wish List" journal. Include how you want to feel, what qualities or skills you'd like to acquire, ideas for ways to have fun, people you want to meet, places you want to go, or things you want to have. Everything. You can add things as more things come to mind. Consider reading a page each night before sleep to keep your vision in mind.

The law of attraction governs all things. Anything you see around you was once a thought. Your frequent thoughts are becoming your reality. Know that the quality of your life is equal to the quality of your consistent thoughts. And you're getting it right!

I give myself permission to fulfill my every whim. I am now achieving all that I desire! *Your turn*: I am

_____.

Has anyone been a great influence in your life or helped you get to where you are?
Perhaps a teacher, mentor, relative, or neighbor? Who are they and what did they teach you or help you with, including the little ways or big opportunities?

_____

_____

_____

_____

_____

_____

_____

_____

Intentions for My Day (Or tomorrow)

What words describe my day? I am feeling _____. I am being _____. I am having _____. I am doing _____. How will I look and feel at the end of the day? Imagine it now.

One of the easiest ways to align my energy with the best possible future for myself is to feel appreciation for anything that feels good to me *now*. I feel very fortunate when I think of my life. No matter where I am or what I'm doing, I can look around and notice things that make me feel that way every day.

What do I love about where I am right now in my life and why? The many things that make me feel fortunate to be who I am are...

_____
_____
_____
_____
_____
_____
_____
_____
_____
_____
_____
_____
_____
_____
_____
_____

What are some things that make me feel fortunate when I look around my home?

_____

What are some things that make me feel fortunate about the work I do?

_____

What are some things that make me feel fortunate about my hobbies or social life?

_____

When I'm in nature, near trees and perhaps water or mountains, what are the words that describe how I feel when I notice its beauty? And what do I love about it? Or is there something else I adore even more?

_____

When I look around when I'm driving or taking a walk, what am I noticing?

_____

What words describe how fortunate I am to be in my body?

_____

When I'm in a wonderful mood and feeling very fortunate, it's the best time to think about my wishes and dreams. With some real enthusiasm, finish these sentences in relation to my goals or dreams:

I *love* how good it feels to know that I can accomplish _____.

I love when I feel like celebrating about my progress on _____.

It feels so good to know that I'm going to _____.

It feels so good to be doing better at _____.

What are the words that describe how fortunate I feel when I think of my future?

_____

_____

_____

What's my favorite part about what I expect to happen for me in the months to come and why is that important to me? Why does it feel good to me? How will it change things for me?

_____

_____

_____

_____

_____

_____

_____

_____

I am deciding right now that I am *forever* rich. And this fortune I have is whatever I believe will make me even happier than I am now. I am full of love and appreciation! *Your turn*: I am

_____.

✱ ＊ ⋯ ＊ ⋯ ＊ ⋯ ✱✱ ⋯ ＊ ⋯ ✱ ⋯ ✱ ⋯ ＊ ⋯ ✱✱ ⋯ ＊ ⋯ ✱ ⋯ ＊ ⋯ ✱ ⋯ ✱✱ ⋯ ＊

How are you feeling about yourself recently?
What's feeling good? If anything feels off balance, how do you want things to be?
How would the best outcome look and feel?

_____

_____

_____

_____

_____

Intentions for My Day (Or tomorrow)

What words describe my day? I am feeling _____. I am being _____. I am having _____. I am doing _____. How will I look and feel at the end of the day? Imagine it now.

The more I radiate positive energy, the more I attract positive people, conversations, and moments throughout my day. I often tell myself that I'm creating more and more positive moments by appreciating this one. Right now I am appreciating...

_____

_____

_____

_____

_____

_____

_____

_____

_____

I feel that my energy is now higher and stronger than any negative forces or energy that's around me. I also have my emotions as a compass that tell me if one direction is better for me to go than another. I use it when I'm deciding what events or conversations I want to take part in. I notice I've been choosing the direction of...

_____

_____

_____

_____

_____

_____

_____

I decided to align with the harmony of my true nature. And I know it's a choice I can make every day. And oh, how I *love* feeling good. With all that I am, and all that I want to be and have and do in my life, I also decided to...

_____

_____

_____

_____

_____

_____

_____

_____

_____

_____

_____

_____

_____

_____

_____

What's it like to know that I'm creating a genuine feeling of blissful wellbeing? What does blissful, pure positive energy feel like to me? Have I noticed that I can breathe in with my attention on my heart center and feel like I'm breathing in something rather heavenly? It's as though there's a blanket of blissful energy being laid upon my chest. Try it now. *Just exhale all the way out, and then breathe in very slowly with your attention on the heart center, or place your palms there.* When I do this throughout my day, it helps me stay in such a good-feeling place. It really makes for a wonderful day. And I love knowing how healing this is to my body. With more practice, it gets better and easier.

No matter what my *life's* goals are, the most important goal for me to have is attuning to the harmony of my true nature or inner spirit. When I put my one-pointed focus on feeling as good as my natural-born energy and wellbeing, I easily come into alignment with anything I want. It's like I'm tuning in to the high frequency of my inner being, and all else falls away. I have a direct route to all the peace, joy, and wellbeing I could ever want.

There's no need to clear away anything or search high and low for just the right circumstances. I will hear the guidance that's always nudging me to follow my path to more joy and wellbeing. It's the good-feeling ideas that show up or pop into my mind that I want to listen to. It's that simple. I just need to trust and surrender to it. The most intriguing, fun, or inspired thoughts or ideas that have come to my mind are...

_____

_____

_____

_____

_____

_____

How does it feel to be so tuned in and connected to myself that it allows me to have a clear mind and feel present in whatever setting I'm in? I am feeling more present when...

_____

_____

_____

The more I practice thoughts, actions, and intentions that align with my true nature, the better I feel. And the better I feel, the more I attract what I truly want. I love when I start seeing the results that show me how powerful my thoughts and intentions really are. *Your turn*: I am _____.

Intentions for My Day (Or tomorrow)

What words describe my day? I am feeling _____. I am being _____. I am having _____. I am doing _____. How will I look and feel at the end of the day? Imagine it now.

How much more am I able to allow blissful wellbeing to flow in and around me? How much more blissful am I able to feel? I want to feel it more than ever, *now* and in the days, weeks, and months ahead. There's no turning back. It's becoming all I know. The only way I know how to be. How much more can I align with it? *List all of the things that you're now becoming, or all the things you're becoming better at every day.*

_____

_____

_____

_____

_____

_____

_____

_____

_____

_____

_____

_____

_____

_____

_____

_____

_____

_____

_____

How many of these things do you feel you are now? Circle them. I bet it's most, if not all. You don't have to wait to become this. You are this now. Your desire is making it so, and all you need to do is practice believing in it. And then put your faith and trust in it. Surrender to it, and it will come.

Once again, just for the fun of it, list all of the things you believe you are magnetic to. I am now attracting...

_____

_____

_____

_____

_____

_____

_____

_____

_____

_____

_____

_____

_____

_____

_____

_____

_____

_____

I am now achieving the feeling of total wellbeing. *Your turn*: I am _____.
Why is it becoming so easy for me to be in charge of my own destiny and wellbeing?

What are you loving and appreciating today about your day or week?
And did anyone do anything to make your life better or easier or more fun? How?

_____

_____

_____

_____

_____

_____

_____

_____

_____

_____

_____

_____

_____

_____

_____

_____

_____

Intentions for My Day (Or tomorrow)

What words describe my day? I am feeling _____. I am being _____. I am having
_____. I am doing _____. How will I look and feel at the end of the day? Imagine it now.

Wellbeing is a part of who I am *now* and always. I am as aligned with joy, wellbeing, and abundance as I let myself be. And I decided to let things be easy for me. Every area of my life is getting better and easier every day in every way. It's going to keep getting better. There's no end to the amount of joy, peace, love, and abundance that I can have in my life.

Why is it so easy for me to feel more wellbeing flowing to me now? How did I get here?
I set these intentions:

_____

_____

_____

_____

_____

_____

I released some old beliefs, continued to make peace with any worries, and found a place of ease by...

_____

_____

_____

_____

_____

I take time to purposely increase my energy and clarity, nurture myself, and practice a state of wellbeing by...

_____

_____

_____

_____

_____

I always think of myself as being in a state of wellbeing, or becoming aligned with a heightened state of wellbeing. Thoughts like...

_____

_____

_____

_____

I am practicing the feeling of anything I wish to achieve until I make it mine. I'm taking the path to my greatest joy and wellbeing. And I know I deserve it!

Why am I feeling so certain that everything in my life is becoming better every day in every way?

_____

_____

Why am I starting to feel so good?

_____

_____

Why do I feel more at ease in my body now?

_____

_____

When did I become so clear-minded? What subjects have I gained clarity on?

_____

_____

Why is it suddenly so easy for me to release unwanted thoughts and beliefs? What have I replaced them with?

_____

_____

Why am I able to be so mindful and present in nearly every moment now? How much more present have I been feeling throughout my day? Where is my favorite place to be present in and why?

_____

_____

How did I get to have so much more energy? What am I doing more of with this energy?

_____

_____

How does it feel to allow myself to feel good all the time? In what ways am I purposely letting myself relax more and where am I when this happens? What am I thinking about that helps me get there?

_____

_____

_____

When did I start feeling so focused and unstoppable in my spirit of peace and wellbeing? I am creating positive change with my natural abilities. And if I speak of myself, I only share the thoughts of wellbeing that I'm focused on. You see, _I become the way I see myself..._

And what I believe I can be, I can be. My thoughts have energy and power to change everything, as I wish it to be. I am on a magnificent life-changing journey that's ongoing. I will never be the same. I am moving forward and upward. It can only get better. _Your turn_: I am _____.

✦ ✦ ˙ · . · ✦ . . ˌ · ˌ ✦✦ . · · ✦ · . . ✦ . . · ˌ ˌ . ✦✦ . · ✦ · . ✦ ✦ · . . ˌ ✦ . . ˌ . ✦✦ . . · ·

Intentions for My Day (Or tomorrow)

What words describe my day? I am feeling _____. I am being _____. I am having _____. I am doing _____. How will I look and feel at the end of the day? Imagine it now.

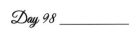

I decided that I am now in the qualities and energy of my blissful wellbeing. I remind myself daily of what these qualities are. Basically, I follow what I believe is required for me to achieve more ease, energy, clarity, and joy. What else am I choosing to be or have or do from this point forward that I believe will align me with my highest level of wellbeing and prosperity? *Finish the sentences below, giving as many answers as you can think of.* From now on, with the best of my intentions:

I *choose* to feel...

_____

_____

_____

_____

_____

I choose to be more...

_____

_____

_____

_____

_____

I choose to have more...

_____

_____

_____

_____

_____

I choose to enjoy more...

_____

_____

_____

_____

_____

I choose to do more ...

_____

_____

_____

_____

Whenever I feel the need to guide myself back to a better feeling state, I think of something like this:

I'm in charge of how I feel.
How do I want to feel today?
How does it feel when I *allow* myself to feel _____? (fill in with however you wish to feel, such as; good, blissful, happy, clear-minded, successful)
Mind, Body, and Spirit, spirit show me how it feels when I allow myself to feel _____.
I feel how my body responds to this suggestion and notice any shift in my energy.
And then I close my eyes, focus on the center of my mind, and think of all the words or phrases that describe the feeling I want or how it feels when I've achieved it.

When stressful situations come up:

I'm in charge of how I react to things.
What's the solution in this situation?
How can I look at this in a different way?
My favorite thing about this is _____.
How do I prefer things to be?
I am deciding right now that it's okay to let this go and expect things to get better.

I redirect any worries or negative thoughts about this by thinking something like:

I choose love, which means I accept whatever's happening.
I may not approve of it, but I can control how I react to it.
If desired, I can do my best to trust that it will work itself out.
I choose wellbeing, which means I care enough about myself to feel good no matter what.
Every day I am better at letting this go.
And I love believing that everything is always working out for me.

To practice a mindset of abundance and attract all that I wish for, I think of things like this:

I am limitless and I choose to be and have and do all that I desire. I am open and receptive to all the gifts that life has to offer me. I love being me, I love my life, I love how good I can feel. I love knowing that all I need to do is be in the joy of who I am and all the answers and my desires are on their way to me. There's no need to search for them. As I stay in a good-feeling place more frequently, all that I desire is falling into place, and all in perfect timing. My blissful wellbeing and limitless abundance is available to me now and I am now achieving an energetic alignment with it, and it must become my reality.

The goal is to make all of my dreams a part of me and to become a part of my dreams until I've achieved them. I am in the energy of them. I feel as though I'm living and breathing it and appreciating it. I'm happy where I am and eager and excited for what's to come! *Your turn*: I am _____.

✳ ✳ . . . ✳ . . . ✳ . . . ✳✳. . . ✳✳ . . . ✳ . . . ✳✳. . . ✳✳ . . . ✳ . . . ✳✳. . . ✳✳ . . . ✳ . . . ✳✳. . . ✳ . .

Intentions for My Day (Or tomorrow)

What words describe my day? I am feeling _____. I am being _____. I am having _____. I am doing _____. How will I look and feel at the end of the day? Imagine it now.

Mind, body, and spirit, it's time to work together in harmony. How does it feel when I'm in a state of blissful wellbeing, with my body, mind, and spirit in harmony with one another? What's it like to have a clear mind, a comfortable body, and understand the true meaning of being in the joy of who I am? Show me how it feels. The words that come to mind are...

_____
_____
_____
_____
_____
_____
_____
_____
_____
_____

When I feel this way, there's no struggle. Anything that felt like that before has been replaced with ease, clarity, joy, and fun. And I feel free!

When I'm feeling blissful every morning and letting it carry me through my day, what's it like to live that way? And how do I feel at the end of the day when everything's gone my way? How does it feel to close my eyes right now and imagine what it's like to get up tomorrow morning and be living it? What's changed in how I go about my day?

_____
_____
_____
_____
_____
_____
_____
_____
_____
_____

I feel more balanced and calm every day because...

_____
_____
_____

I feel healthier every day because...

_____
_____
_____

I feel more fearless and free every day because...

_____

_____

_____

I feel more abundant every day because...

_____

_____

_____

What are some powerful words I can use to describe myself when I'm feeling focused and unstoppable in my spirit of peace and wellbeing? All I know is that the forward direction of my thoughts and desires are creating my best life, and it feels...

_____

_____

_____

_____

_____

_____

When I am feeling focused and unstoppable in my spirit of peace and wellbeing:

All that I desire is flowing to me as I transform my thoughts.
All that I desire is flowing to me as I believe in me.
All that I desire is flowing to me as I believe in my wellbeing.
All that I desire is flowing to me as I make it a part of me.
This blissful feeling of wellness is a part of who I am.
I feel it flowing to me, and I expect it to keep flowing to me.
I continue making peace with myself and anything I ever allowed to cause me worry.
I only associate myself with words of wellness now.
I am focused on blissful wellbeing and feeling fully aligned with it.
And I love being an example of joy and wellbeing to others.

When I decide to achieve any goal and practice the feeling of what I want as though it's mine right now, it becomes so. I am now achieving a deeply satisfying life that supports my total and blissful wellbeing.

★ I Am Focused & Unstoppable in My Spirit of Peace & Wellbeing

Intentions for My Day (Or tomorrow)

What words describe my day? I am feeling _____. I am being _____. I am having _____. I am doing _____. How will I look and feel at the end of the day? Imagine it now.

A WISH Moment for Inspiration
Words Inspire Spiritual Harmony

You are so good at being in charge of how you feel that you can use any word or action to anchor in the way you wish to feel, any time you want.

1-2-3, Mind, Body, and Spirit, it's time to be in harmony with one another. Show me how it feels.

On the count of three I'm going to breathe in and say "**Harmony**," and when I say that it means that in that moment I decided that I will feel my mind, body, and spirit unite in a blissful feeling of wellbeing, freedom, and limitless abundance.

My body will feel relaxed and energized at the same time, completely free of resistance. My mind will feel clear and spacious with blissful clarity, and my head will feel lighter. My spirit will be completely free.

Slowly breathe in, **1-2-3 Harmony**. Actively breathing with the whole body, I'm calling light to myself, my eyelids, forehead, face, and body are softening...even softer.....twice as soft, slowing down my breath, my mind is transforming thoughts to blissful clarity. I feel the energy in and around my face becoming lighter and freer, clear and spacious mind...clearing right now, *breathing in* wellbeing, joy, freedom, limitless abundance. I am full of energy, feeling limitless, feeling lighter and brighter, feeling blissfully happy and free.

And very slowly, show me one last time...how does it feel when I *allow* myself to feel blissful? Breathe it in.

Show me how it feels when I *allow* myself to feel lighter and freer. Breathe in.

Show me how it feels when I *allow* myself to have a clear mind. Breathing in violet light.

And show me how it feels to have more energy than I did a moment ago. Breathe it in to *every* cell.

How does it feel when I *allow* myself to have twice as much energy than I do right now? *Deep* breath.

How does it feel to have twice as much *clarity* than I did a moment ago?

Lastly, show me how it feels when I *allow* myself to feel even happier than I was a moment ago.

I am in harmony with all that is.

The next time I breathe in and think of the word harmony, I will feel an immediate shift in my energy and feel lighter and freer.

Thank you, my Mind, Body, and Spirit for allowing this blissful wellbeing to stay with me today, and come back to me anytime I call upon it by thinking 1-2-3 **Harmony**. This is my powerful intention.

Additionally, you can practice seeing the word "harmony" written over your head and heart and anywhere on your body to allow ease and replace any stress, physical discomfort, or a negative thought.

Just like pressing a button, the moment you put your attention somewhere and think of the word "harmony," you're deciding right then to immediately release what's happening and allow yourself to feel good.

★ I Am More Aligned With Blissful Wellbeing Every Day

Day 100 _____

I Am Getting Better Every Day in Every Way

What is your favorite part about where you are right now in these areas?

My Health is: _____

My Mind is: _____

My Body looks and feels: _____

I Am Feeling: _____

My Home and Family are: _____

My Relationship is: _____

My Personal Life is: _____

My Work Life is: _____

My Dreams and Plans are: _____

My Life in general is: _____

For each area, write down one or more things that you intend to continue or start doing differently that you believe will support your wellbeing in the days, weeks, or months ahead. If a new habit is desired, consider setting a date to start this or put a reminder in your calendar to follow up when you're ready.

My Health: _____

My Mind: _____

My Body: _____

How I'm Feeling: _____

My Home or Family: _____

My Relationship: _____

My Personal Time: _____

My Work Life: _____

My Dreams and Plans: _____

My Ideal Future: _____

What is making you feel happy right now and what are you looking forward to?

_____

_____

_____

_____

My mind, body, and spirit are now working in harmony with one another and I am a cooperative component. I am in charge of how my life goes and I am choosing to spend every precious moment of it in loving appreciation to attract all that I wish for. Inner guidance, *thank you* for helping me do this!

I am as happy as I let myself be. I am feeling fortunate to be where I am and excited for even better things to come for me. The following is becoming instilled in my mind and I feel it with *all* my heart:

> *By nature, I am in a state of blissful wellbeing. And by* nature, I have the ability to be, and have, and do *all* that I desire. As I am *true* to my nature, I'm feeling the way I'm meant to feel. I am in *love* with life. I am *confident* and at ease. I am aligning with a state of *blissful* wellbeing. And I am *limitless.*

I am now attracting more good things into my life and I intend to have *way* more fun. I smile my way through my day and see my desires coming to life *right* before my eyes. I intend to practice feeling this way and create the joyful and abundant life I was born to live.

I am holding a mental picture of myself in the highest level of joy and wellbeing and it's *who I am now.* How does it feel to be in the qualities and energy that attracts all my desires?

Here are some more questions for you, as well as some suggestions for continued success in achieving more joy and wellbeing:

Answer these questions when you're feeling your best. Consider using this as your main focus and repeating this exercise in a blank journal, weekly or as desired. Or perhaps you could use a symbol of each of your goals or dreams and tell it what you appreciate about it. As you know, it gets you feeling like it's yours now. It may even help you dream of it and wake up in that abundant energy if it's done right before going to sleep.

What is every aspect you love about being in your natural state of blissful wellbeing and why?

_____

_____

_____

_____

_____

What is every aspect you love about having clarity of mind and why?

_____

_____

_____

_____

_____

What is every aspect you love about having your body full of harmony and why?

_____

_____

_____

_____

What is every aspect you love about having an even happier home life and why?

_____

_____

_____

_____

_____

What is every aspect you love about having an even happier relationship/dating or single life and why?

_____

_____

_____

_____

_____

What is every aspect you love about having a fulfilling work life and why?

_____

_____

_____

_____

_____

What is every aspect you love about having an amazing personal life and why?

_____

_____

_____

_____

_____

What is every aspect you love about having a deeply satisfying life and why?

_____

_____

_____

_____

_____

What is every aspect you love about letting yourself feel good and align with all of this with effortless ease?

_____

_____

_____

_____

Do your very best to continue guiding your thoughts with more purpose. Here's more practice:

When I trust that all is well with me and always will be, I release all resistance and it frees me. I am creating amazing outcomes and opportunities for myself. If I ever feel stressed or concerned about anything, I can think of the words "I trust and surrender" or "I am full of love and harmony," or whatever resonates with me.

I also remind myself often that my body responds to my suggestions, requests or commands. I can think things like:

- ★ How much more clarity can I have right now? Mind, show me how it feels when I slow my breath and clear my thoughts.
- ★ How much calmer can I feel? Nervous system or body, show me how it feels when I allow myself to be completely relaxed and calm.
- ★ How much more energy can I have right now? How much more vitality can I breathe into my body and my breath?

If desired, here are some more questions you can ask yourself daily to help you stay in a good-feeling place and continue on your path to more joy and wellbeing:

How much more at ease can I feel in my body and my breath?
How much more harmony can I feel in my body and my breath?
How much more clarity can I have today?
How much more abundance can I feel around me?
How much more energy and vitality can I feel in my body and my breath?
How much more energy can I feel flowing to every cell in my body?
Body, show me how it feels, now and in the days and weeks and months ahead.

If you want to align with a desire, but don't yet believe in it or believe it will happen easily, it will still come along if you put your attention on something else that *is* going well. But you can also simply think about how it feels to have it come easily and why you love it. I want to allow blissful wellbeing to come to me easily because...

_____

_____

_____

_____

_____

_____

I love feeling blissfully happy because...

_____

_____

I also like knowing it's okay when I'm not there. The best thing I can do then is take the next gentle step to feeling just a little better. It's great to know I never have to get mad at myself. I'm just letting myself be.

Consider writing out any signs or synchronicities that show you the results of your frequent thoughts. Noticing and appreciating them can help your desires manifest more quickly. Here is a journal prompt to get you started: *I love when the universe and law of attraction shows me results of my positive thoughts and high-vibin' energy. I have been seeing, feeling, or having experiences like...*

If desired, 1) Make note of anything you practiced in the past ten days that felt good to you and you wish to continue. 2) Add your favorite thought-provoking question and affirmation to the list you started. And now you should have ten or more questions and affirmations to refer to on your list. If desired, continue practicing them and create new ones as new desires form. Practiced thought = belief = the feeling of it being a part of you = becomes your reality. As you further your self-discovery, more layers of your true nature are revealed to you.

Mind and body, thank you for working with me to bring more harmony, balance, and joy into my life. I intend to do my part to provide the ease and relaxation, and laughter and love that I know will help me achieve this. I love feeling good!

Dear Mind,

You are functioning perfectly and always respond to my direction, and brilliantly so. Each day I remind myself that you are stable and strong and keeping me calm, balanced, and full of joy. Thank you for working with me to achieve harmony of our mind, body, and spirit.

Dear Body,

You are functioning perfectly and know how to bring yourself back into balance, again and again. Thank you for maintaining my total wellbeing. I am aware of how you're feeling and listening for anything you may need to help you keep that balance.

Dear Inner Spirit,

Thank you for your guidance and love and the lighthearted spirit that dwells within me. Thank you for helping me guide my thoughts and emotions to align with your pure positive energy. You allow me to feel the blissful wellbeing that's available to me.

Dear Self,

It's time for me to stay in a good-feeling place. Total wellbeing is my birthright and it's natural to me. My only "job" is to believe in it, and then stay out of the way. That just means I'm letting myself be at ease and in the joy of who I am more of the time. And that's what I intend to do.

Dear Blissful Wellbeing,

Thank you for being mine. I intend to breathe you in each and *every* day. And, *oh*, how truly wonderful you feel. I love knowing that you'll always be a part of me, and that I can tune in to you any time I wish. I'm going to practice it until I feel that you're with me all day, every day.

I move forward with faith and trust in my ability to become anything I believe I can be.

★ I Am Now Achieving Blissful Wellbeing

How does it feel to be a vibrational match to blissful wellbeing?

How does it feel to be your magnificent self?

Why is it so easy for you to achieve more of what you want now?

Congratulations! You made it all the way to Day 100!

This is what I wish for you now or when the time is right for you:

> You've set yourself free from any worry or struggle.
> You've become your own best friend.
> You're allowing yourself to feel the blissful wellbeing flowing to you.
> You are now achieving vibrational alignment with your desire for a higher level of wellbeing.
> Your wishes for a more blissful life are coming true, and the better you feel, the better it will be.
> It's all yours. It's available to you.
> It's time. You're ready.
> You have a strong desire for it.
> You believe in it. You're feeling it.
> You're energetically aligned with it. It's done.
> There is no limit to what you can be, or have, or do.
> I wish you *more*. More of everything you wish for.

I hope this book has helped you on your life's journey to feel a little (or a lot) more happy and free, as you were born to be!

All your wishes and desires are finding their way to you. Just allow yourself to be at ease with all of it, and it will come. All in perfect timing. Hold that thought, have faith it will come, believe in it, and let it be.

If you're looking to further your journey of self-discovery, keep an eye out for the next two workbooks in the series; *Dear Freedom* and *Dear Wishes & Dreams*. There's also a journal series to come at the time of this writing. Character-building children's books are also in the works!

One Last Pep Talk

Every day I choose to be in the qualities of the person I was born to be. Any time I feel off, I just ask myself:

How does it feel to allow myself to feel blissful? How much more harmony can I feel in my body and my breath?

My body will respond to my questions. I will feel the answers. I will feel a shift in my energy. With more practice I am feeling the pulsation of that energy.

To get a bigger response, I ask more questions, such as: How does it feel to be in the harmony of my mind, body, and spirit? How does it feel to have all of my energies in balance? How does it feel to have tremendous inner strength and courage? How does that feel? How does it feel to be aligned with all my desires?

How does it feel to raise my vibration with these questions? What's it like to feel free to be at ease with myself and all that is? And to know that I was born to live in joy and abundance? How does it feel to be magnetic to all that I wish for? And to know that it's all coming?

How does it feel to be really good at being my authentic self?

What else am I good at?
I'm really good at practicing, practicing, practicing.
And being one with the energy of anything I want to bring into my reality.
I am great at supporting myself, loving myself, and being my own cheerleader.
I am great at doing everything I do in a great way. The way that I choose to. The way that feels good to me.
I am the master of my mind and my thoughts. I am the master of my life.

I love using my ability to guide my thoughts to feel how I want to feel. And I say thank you. Thank you for all the amazing experiences and emotions I've had before now that guide me to follow my most joyful path.

Blissful wellbeing is a part of me now and always. My alignment with all my desires is inevitable. I am now in the magnificent joy of who I am as I revel in the delicious anticipation of all the great things that are coming my way.

I believe in myself. I feel the value of getting to be who I am. I love the way I think and feel. I love knowing what I know. I love that I cherish my thoughts and ideas. I love knowing that I can do anything.

I can choose how I want to feel. I can choose what I want to do. I get to choose what I believe and what I invite into my life. I can create any feeling and any reality I want to exist in. I am using my creative mind to be what I want to be. I can see it, feel it, taste it, and touch it, and it's mine.

I am now feeling as happy and free as I can be, and the more I accept or appreciate what *is* and have faith that it's all becoming better in time, the more I'll stay in a harmonious place of ease and joy. **It's in this place where I fully align with my blissful wellbeing, my freedom, and my every wish.**

Thank you so much...

For reading this book! I hope you enjoyed it and will continue to benefit from having read it. If you're interested in continued support or being notified about my upcoming courses, workbooks or journal series, as well as any giveaways, please visit our website https://wishmorewellness.com/ and subscribe to the mailing list or follow my author page.

I would also appreciate it so much if you would
please **consider giving your honest review** of this book on Amazon. It's very helpful to an author's success, and it would mean so much to me.

Thank you in advance!

WHAT'S NEXT?

More WORKBOOKS and a JOURNAL SERIES...

Join my website mailing list or follow me on Amazon here amazon.com/author/susanbalogh to receive updates on new releases!

PLEASE also share your success stories with me!
Be sure to join the Wish*More Wellness Facebook Group
so you can share any milestones or achievements that manifest for you,
or feel free to email me at suebalogh@wishmorewellness.com.

Share the Love & Gift a Friend!

Do you know someone who could use this book?

You can gift the Kindle version directly into their email inbox. Just choose the Amazon purchase option "Buy for Others."

★★★ The Wish*More Wellness Project ★★★

Please help us grow a community of uplifters by sharing your milestones and success stories to encourage others to believe in their ability to create the life they wish for and go after their dreams. Use the hashtag #wishmorewellness on social media when posting about your achievements and share it with the Wishmore Wellness Facebook Group. Thank you for helping to create more wellbeing!

I invite you to preview my first book.
It's been called "life-changing," "enlightening," "magical," and "fun."

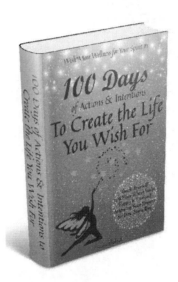

100 Days of Actions & Intentions to Create the Life You Wish For

"Imagine meeting a best friend each day, someone who always has your best interests at heart, someone who has great conversations that help you heal and flourish. This book is like having that best friend, day after day, being a loving companion helping you to heal and be well. I am going to use this book to help me make a lifetime habit of creating a life I desire, day after day after day."

~ **Dr. Aloha Lavina, Managing Director of Arkipelago Consulting**

"Oh, it had me at the front cover. I loved the bite-sized, the idea of reading a book one page/day at a time. If you like being interactive with your books and you like adding a touch of magic to your life, this book is ideal. A little cracker to forever keep on the shelf and you can do it as many times as you like."

~ **Dr. Jennifer Meyer, meyersamuse.com**

"Thought provoking and inspirational! This is a great little book that is very positive, upbeat and inspirational. It is written so that you can read it in short bursts made up of 100 small chapters."

~ **Scott B. Allan, Bestselling author and top 500 reviewer**

"This book inspires to take action every day. From the powerful start with a "Promise to Myself" pledge, through action steps to take towards a renewed mindset, and intentional shaping of our own future and well being. Definitely a great way of starting the day and setting the stage for success."

~ **Agi Kadar, FDN, CES, healthbalanced.com**

Recommended Reading

Genie in Your Genes: Epigenetic Medicine and the New Biology of Intention
by Dawson Church

The Great Little Book of Afformations
by Noah St. John

The Hidden Messages in Water
by Masaru Emoto

Ho'oponopono: The Hawaiian Forgiveness Ritual as the Key to Your Life's Fulfillment
by Ulrich E. Duprée

The Law of Attraction: The Basics of the Teachings of Abraham
by Esther Hicks

The Science of Being Well
by Wallace D. Wattles

The Seven Spiritual Laws of Success: A Practical Guide to the Fulfillment of Your Dreams
by Deepak Chopra

The Wisdom of Your Cells: How Your Beliefs Control Your Biology
by Bruce H. Lipton

I also highly recommend guided meditations by Sanaya Roman or Alexander and Kenneth Soares.

If you'd like to learn more Qi Gong and experience the amazing health benefits it offers, I highly recommend Qi Gong for Self-Healing (DVD) or Qi Gong for More Energy by Lee Holden. I received my Qi Gong teacher certification through him and I find his teaching style easy, thorough, and uplifting. I also include my own Qi Gong videos in the 12-week course I offer.

At 83, my skeptic mother felt better after just three of his Qi Gong sessions, and she was experiencing a pretty severe back injury pain at the time. I looked into teaching it soon after that and never looked back. Regular practice has brought many people back to good health after a serious illness, even those who were not expected to improve.

The key is simply to find something *you* enjoy that puts your mind and body at ease, and do it as often as you can, if not daily. Before you know it, you will be in the most wonderful-feeling place you've ever been. And you'll never look back.

★ Also By Susan Balogh ★

BOOKS
100 Days of Actions & Intentions to Create the Life You Wish For
https://www.amazon.com/dp/B099PZC9T1

There's MAGIC in this MANIFESTING JOURNAL: It's Your Imagination
http://amzn.com/B0967TRMSF

FREE MINI-WORKSHOP
3 Steps to Wellbeing & Achieving Your Dreams
https://courses.wishmorewellness.com/courses/Mini-Workshop-3-Steps

ONLINE COURSE
Create the Life You Wish For: A 100-Day Course
https://courses.wishmorewellness.com

ONLINE SERVICES
1:1 Coaching for Mindset/Happiness/Manifesting
Positive EFT Coaching (Meridian Tapping)
Energy Healing, Guided Meditation
Reiki I & II and Master/Teacher Certification
All or part available by video conference

★ ★ ★

All of the above are available at
wishmorewellness.com/services/
Find us on Instagram @Wishmore_Wellness
https://www.instagram.com/wishmore_wellness/
Please join the Wishmore Wellness Facebook Group
https://www.facebook.com/groups/2061444523962316

About the Author

Susan Balogh is a holistic healing and happiness coach, author, and speaker who has a passion for helping others tap into their true power to achieve any state of mind that allows them to achieve their goals and dreams.

With a desire to heal herself and help others, Susan sought training for over 20 years in many healing modalities and learned how to turn pain and struggle into what she calls blissful wellbeing!

In her first book, *100 Days of Actions and Intentions to Create the Life You Wish For,* Susan loves to evoke every possible emotion from her readers to help them reach their full potential.

Susan is from Western New York, but travels the country in her custom (and very pink) RV to provide donation-based teaching. She had a vision of doing this for a couple years before leaving her 20-year hospital job. She also happens to love driving *anywhere* for *any* reason.

When she's not behind the wheel or writing or coaching, you might find her walking, biking, making jewelry, or spending time with family. She is a certified Reiki Master/Teacher, Qi Gong instructor, and happiness coach. More information about Susan and her offerings can be found at www.wishmorewellness.com.

Set Yourself Free & Be Happy!

You're perfect and exactly where you're meant to be in your life right now and constantly becoming more of who you truly are, and will always be moving toward a better place.

All good things come your way with effortless ease. The possibilities are limitless.

This is only the beginning, and you're moving forward and upward on your journey of life.

Let each kind word, thought, and action begin with you and create a better life for you and those around you, one moment at a time.

Wishing you freedom, love & all that you wish for.

Susan

Wheresoever you go, go with all your heart – *Confucius*

Made in the USA
Coppell, TX
18 February 2023

13028929R00120